Dream Workbook

Julia Gentry

UNINHIBITED
PUBLISHING

DENVER

Dream Workbook: A Guide to Greater Spiritual Awakening and Alignment
Published by Uninhibited Publishing
Denver, CO

ISBN: 978-1-7357859-1-2
SELF-HELP / Spiritual

Interior design by Victoria Wolf, wolfdesignandmarketing.com
Cover art by Maria Barry
Cover Design by Donna Cunningham at BeauxArts.Design

QUANTITY PURCHASES: Schools, companies, professional groups, clubs, and other organizations may qualify for special terms when ordering quantities of this title. For information, email julia@thedreamfactoryandco.com.

UNINHIBITED
PUBLISHING

CONTENTS

HOW TO USE THIS GUIDE
"Is there something more?"

If you have ever found yourself asking the question, "Is there something more?" then you, my friend, are a dreamer in waiting, a dreamer who is ready to wake up!

Too often, we blame "life" for stopping us from living our dreams, but *if life is stopping you from living the dream, what's the point of life?*

Perhaps it's not that life is getting in the way of you living your dream, but maybe it's that you don't have a dream that's louder than your life to live for!

Dream as if you'll live forever
Live as if you'll die tomorrow

DREAM Workbook is designed to be a companion piece as you move through my book, *DREAM—I Dare You.*

It is designed to be a step-by-step guide to support you in greater spiritual awakening and alignment.

It is designed to give you the space to "go in," to still the chatter of the mind, and to access the quiet places within your heart so your dreams can speak.

It's designed to take you even deeper.

I admit my book *DREAM—I Dare You* is a lot. Like, a lot, a lot. And truth be told, the journey of dreaming is a lot. Learning to be still in a loud world, creating new habits, building new beliefs, and learning about yourself and God in a limitless way *is* a lot.

So really, I guess you could say this workbook is designed to help you digest a lot, a little bit at a time.

> **As my dad always said, "How do you eat an elephant?"**
>
> **And I would always say, "One bite at a time."**
>
> **Now I say to you, *how do you accomplish your dreams?***
>
> ***One bite at a time.***

With that being said, there are a couple of things I want you to take note of to maximize your experience with this workbook, as well as your overall dreaming process:

I encourage you to use this workbook as a *companion* piece to solidify what you learn in my book *DREAM—I Dare You.* As you read through each chapter of the book, you will use the complimentary chapters within this workbook to go even deeper within yourself, one bite at a time, one chapter at a time. Read each book chapter **first.** Do the corresponding workbook chapter **second.**

You will see in each of the chapters within this workbook that I will reiterate and review the overarching themes and most important takeaways from *DREAM—I Dare You.* It's a bit repetitive in nature for a reason. Research has shown that you only have to read something once to understand it but three to four times to memorize it. If I can get you to reread the most important themes and concepts a couple of different times, it will serve you in not just understanding it but also memorizing it!

You will also notice that though I do provide the same questions straight from the book, only with more space to write, I have additionally and purposefully expounded upon these by adding questions beyond what you'll find in my book. Some of these questions may seem basic but, believe me, they're not. They're each deserving of your answer, which means none of this is rhetorical. It's important that you don't skip over these questions, nor do I want you to just think about your answers. I want you to write about your answers. Research has shown that we have a major increase in retention when we actually *handwrite* notes instead of just read them or even type them. It actually increases neural activity in certain sections of the brain, similar to meditation. This workbook is designed to give you the space to help you hear your dreams while also giving you the space to write them down, partially so you won't forget them and also as a bit of accountability so you can stay true to your dreams and boldly chase the life God intended for you to live.

At the end of each chapter, I have included additional scriptures and a prayer. Both my book and this workbook are designed to not only support you in creating stronger mental and emotional well-being but also to support you in your own spiritual growth. This allows for full integration. Most people think that "being spiritual" is about being religious. It's not. Spirituality is so much more than the box we try to compartmentalize it in. God is so much more magnificent than our minds could ever conceive. Yet wherever you are in your spiritual journey, whether you believe in God with your whole heart or you're just simply curious because our world is crazy and you need something or someone to believe in, I believe that this workbook is going to be instrumental in your journey. Why? Because I believe God Himself is going to show up for you. He is going to meet you wherever you are. You are not too far gone, you are not too old, you are not too young, you are exactly where you need to be. I believe you are going to see visions and dream dreams! I believe you are going to see wonders in the heavens above and signs on the earth below. And in the pages to come, I encourage you to capture it all!

Then when each chapter is complete, I want you to apply it to your everyday life. I want you to *live like it.* You'll notice that every chapter is written in a way to explore all the ways to incorporate this work into your day-to-day life. When you make the connection between what you're learning and how you actually *live* your life, true change happens. The Bible says, "Give me understanding and I will obey your instructions; I will put them into practice with all my heart" (Psalm 119:34, New Living Translation). I don't want you just to read this; I want you to put it into practice. I want you to step out in faith, and I want you to take steps toward your greatest dreams every single day.

And last but not least, I want to encourage you to use my book and this workbook as an opportunity to come together with other people who can join you on the journey, whether that's in a book club, a small group, or simply an impromptu gathering. Though every question is designed for your own personal alignment, it is also designed to open discussion and conversation with other people in a group setting because there is so much power in gathering together. The Bible says, "For where two or three gather in my name, there I am with them" (Matthew 18:20). So whether you join or start a gathering, whether you decide to gather with your spouse and kids, a circle of friends, or even work associates, I encourage you to dream together. To learn more about **DREAM: Gather**, go to TheDreamFactoryandCo.com/dream-book.

Now, may the mind blow begin.

Introduction

Pages 1–13

Did you know that the world needs your dreams?

Do you believe that the world is actually *waiting* for your dreams?

Why? Because the world needs the very dreams God's put within you to manifest themselves in the world around us. For every problem we see today, for every heartache we're experiencing, for every injustice, wrongdoing, upside-down system, there are solutions. Only those solutions don't lie dormant in the world around us; they lie dormant in the world within us.

That means it is time for a massive wake-up call to ignite each and every one of us to be the light in the dark, the salt of the earth, to live awake and aligned with what heaven is doing.

"Very truly I tell you, whoever believes in me will do the works I have been doing, and they will do even greater things than these" (John 14:12-14).

Have you ever considered that you could do even greater things than what Jesus did? This is not a question to downplay *Him* in any way but rather to recognize the power *you* have within you because of the Holy Spirit. That's His gift that has been given to you!

Have you ever considered that the very dreams you're dreaming actually could be the solutions to some of the world's greatest problems? Or at least could enhance the lives of those around you? Why or why not?

_____

_____

_____

_____

I'd like for you to consider life on a larger scale for just a moment and, as you do, answer the following questions:

What problems are you seeing today that keep you up at night or worried throughout the day?

_____

_____

_____

_____

What heartaches are you (or others) experiencing that are in need of healing?

_____

_____

_____

_____

_____

What type of injustice are you seeing in the world around you?

_____

_____

_____

_____

_____

What type of wrongdoing or upside-down systems need to be corrected for the greater good?

_____

_____

_____

_____

_____

Who do you believe is responsible for bringing solutions to these issues? And why?

_____

_____

_____

_____

_____

Do you believe that you are the "you" that Matthew 5:13-16 is referring to?
Why or why not?

_____

_____

_____

_____

_____

**Your dreams are the solutions to the
world's greatest problems.**

Are you living "salty?" Are *you* are a light to this world, actively pointing people to God? Why or why not?

_____

_____

_____

_____

_____

_____

_____

_____

"You are the salt of the earth but if the salt loses its saltiness, how can it be made salty again … You are the light of the world. A town built on a hill cannot be hidden. Neither do people light a lamp and put it under a bowl. Instead, put it on a stand, and it gives light to everyone in the house. In the same way, let your light shine before others, that they may see your good deeds and praise your Father in heaven" (Matthew 5:13–16).

It *has* to start with you. It *has* to start with me. If not *us*, who? If not you, *who*?

The Bible says, "*Everything* is possible for those who *believe*" (Mark 9:23 [emphasis mine]).

It doesn't say some things. It doesn't say a few things. It says *everything*.

It says that everything is possible for those who what? *Believe.*

These are two very powerful words that we really need to look at: *everything* and *believe.*

Define everything (in your own words).

_____

_____

_____

_____

_____

Define believe (in your own words).

_____

_____

_____

_____

Are you seeing *everything*, according to your definition, play out in your life? Expound. If so, how so? If not, why not?

_____

_____

_____

_____

Would you say that you actually live life like you *believe*? Why or why not?

_____

_____

_____

_____

Do you *believe* that *everything* is possible? Or a better question to ask is, do you *believe* that *your* dreams are possible? Why or why not?

_____

_____

_____

_____

The Bible says, "Truly I tell you, if you have faith as small as a mustard seed, you can say to this mountain, 'Move from here to there,' and it will move. Nothing will be impossible for you" (Matthew 17:20). This tells us there is one prerequisite to "moving mountains"—you must *believe.*

The book of James gives us an even clearer direction on how to believe. It says, "You **must** believe **and not doubt**, because the one who doubts is like a wave of the sea, blown and tossed by the wind" (James 1:6 [emphasis mine]).

Most of us admit, "I believe … well, on most days."

My point exactly.

Doubt is interesting because it doesn't actually mean unbelief. It means *undecided in belief.* It's one thing to not believe (unbelief). It's another to be undecided in your belief (doubt). This is what makes doubt so exhausting; it's the back and forth, up and down, "I believe," "No I don't," "I think it's possible," "Maybe it's not possible," etc.

Most spend more time wondering if it's possible than living their lives as though it is. When you boil it all down, it's not that what you want is "impossible," it's not that you can't, it's not that your dreams are too big, it's that you're spending more time struggling with your own doubt than you are actually pursuing the prize. It's your own doubt getting in the way of your very own belief.

But what if your doubt was an opportunity?! Instead of being tossed here and there, why not use it as an opportunity to decide if you believe. Doubt, therefore, is actually a good thing because it's giving you the opportunity to pick a side! It's signaling you to choose.

Sure, other people may say that it's impossible, but what do you say? Other people may say that you can't, but what do *you* say?

**Doubt is not unbelief;
it is undecided belief.**

For just a moment, I want you to consider this: Could it be your doubt that is keeping you from manifesting your greatest dreams come true? Could it be your doubt that is keeping you from seeing mountains move? Expound.

_____

_____

_____

_____

Are you ready to *believe*? Are you ready to see visions? Are you ready to dream dreams?

_____

_____

_____

Truth be told, it's really hard to see visions and dreams, let alone manifest them when your doubt is manipulating your perspective. And you'll know if your doubt is manipulating your perspective because you won't be seeing or manifesting your greatest visions and dreams in the world around you. If you aren't actively demonstrating this type of power in all areas of life, then it means you are out of alignment, which means there is a disconnect and the greatest way to re-establish alignment is by dreaming.

It's been said that the best time to plant a tree is twenty years ago, the next best time? Today!

You may not be seeing visions come to pass. You may not be living your life's dreams, heck, you may not even know what those are, but that's why we're here. That's why you're reading this book and investing your time in this workbook, to learn how to dream because in doing so, you can literally bridge the gap between what you currently have in life and what you really want most, to turn any midlife crisis—no matter what age you are—into a midlife awakening that sets you free to live your life, consciously.

Are you ready to let your dreams blow your doubt out of the water?

Are you really ready to manifest your dreams?

Are you ready to bring your slice of heaven to this earth?

If so, then let's set an intention. Consider this question: What is the greatest gift you hope to receive in your journey to dreaming? You close the very last page of the book and this workbook, and what is the one thing (or maybe a handful of things) you want most?

_____

_____

_____

_____

Once you've considered your intention, on the next page, I'd like you to take a step to mark your commitment to yourself and this journey!

In dreaming, you actually wake up to your life, not only reconnecting with yourself but also with God who lives *in* you. In dreaming, you bring heaven to earth!

Commitment To Myself

I, _____, commit myself to this journey of living the life of my dreams and no longer settling for "ok," "fine," and "good enough." I commit to live boldly chasing the life God intended despite the fear, doubt, criticism, and, yes, even when I don't know how.

I, _____, commit to offer myself more grace because though change is something I desire, it is hard, and I will need to give myself grace to obtain and sustain my dreams. I commit to taking care of my mind, body, and heart throughout this entire process, and I will remember that this is just that, a process, so I will not demand instant results but, rather, lasting results.

I, _____, commit to getting in alignment with myself and with God. I commit to dreaming God's dreams for my life. I commit to living big, dreaming real, getting loud, and being bold!

I, _____, commit to my community and the people I decide to do this work with. I commit to letting them support me and challenge me while doing the same for them. Because let's be honest, it's more fun to live in a world where we are all chasing our dreams.

I, _____, commit to seeing. I commit to knowing. I commit to playing an active role in bringing heaven to this earth.

My greatest intention in the coming weeks is:

_____
Signature

_____
Date

Additional Scriptures

TO MEDITATE ON AND CONSIDER:

"In the last days, God says, I will pour out my Spirit on all the people. Your sons and daughters will prophesy, your young men will see visions, your old men will dream dreams. Even on my servants, both men and women, I will pour out my Spirit in those days, and they will prophesy. I will show wonders in the heavens above and signs on the earth below, blood and fire and billows of smoke. The sun will be turned to darkness and the moon to blood before the coming of the great and glorious day of the Lord. And everyone who calls on the name of the Lord will be saved" (Acts 2:17–20).

"For the creation waits in eager expectation for the children of God to be revealed" (Romans 8:19).

"But the righteous are as bold as a lion" (Proverbs 28:1).

"Then you will call on me and come and pray to me, and I will listen to you" (Jeremiah 29:12).

"For God hath not given us the spirit of fear; but of power, and of love, and of a sound mind" (2 Timothy 1:7, KJV).

What do these scriptures reveal about the heart of God?

What do these scriptures mean to you?

How could you apply these scriptures to support you in your own journey of dreaming?

Closing Prayer

Dear God,

As the eyes of my heart are awakened, and I am beginning to see things as they really are, I ask that You go with me, before me, and behind me in this journey. I ask that You forgive me and help me in my areas of doubt and unbelief. I commit to seeing. I commit to knowing. I commit to playing an active role in bringing heaven to this earth. I commit to being in alignment with You. I commit to flowing with You. I commit to hearing Your voice. I commit to dreaming Your dreams. In Jesus's name, amen.

Section 1

CHAPTER 1

Define Dreaming

Pages 15–28

Dreaming is a lot like dating.

Let's be real; dating is awkward at first.

But the manifestation of true love is one of life's greatest miracles. And just like the path of true love, in all its awkwardness, joy, pain, and, yes, even disappointments, dreaming, too, is one of life's greatest miracles.

Regardless of where you stand today or your opinions about the topic of dreaming, regardless of your history, your stories, experiences, expectations, upbringing, social status, political views, or favorite flavor of ice cream, you are curious. You recognize that you probably need a few more dreams to come true in your life if you're going to get the most out of this life. But where do you start? How do you even make the time to create the life you've always dreamed of? First, we must be very clear about what dreaming actually is.

What is *your* current definition of dreaming?

_____

_____

_____

_____

_____

Does this "truth" you have about dreaming serve you? If so, can you commit to keeping it? If it doesn't serve you, can you commit to a new truth about dreaming that will serve you?

_____

_____

_____

_____

After much research, working with hundreds of people on this topic, and countless hours on my knees in prayer, my definition of dreaming is:

Great and intense focus, with deep absorption of thought, in a different realm that brings about possibilities with the consideration of those around you.

Take some time and expound on what that definition, bit by bit, piece by piece, means to you.

Great and intense focus …

_____

_____

… with deep absorption of thought …

_____

_____

… in a different realm …

_____

_____

… that brings about possibilities …

_____

_____

… with the consideration of those around you.

_____

_____

If you remember, I mentioned my experience in the RV where the word "DREAM" painted overhead, and all the people who were once asleep to their lives woke up! At first, I ignored this dream. It felt too far out there, too vulnerable to share. Maybe you can relate and feel as though you have hidden your dreams for quite a while. I'd like you to dig those up for a moment and consider the dreams that you've put on the shelf for fear of what other people think, or maybe because "life has gotten in the way," or for any other reason. What dreams do you need to "take off the shelf?"

_____

_____

_____

_____

Despite failure or success, acceptance or rejection, right or wrong, what do you wish for your life?

_____

_____

_____

_____

If dreaming is your ticket to anything you need, at any time, in any way you can fathom or imagine, where do *you* want to go?

_____

_____

_____

_____

_____

_____

What's most important to you?

_____

_____

_____

_____

_____

_____

Dreaming is the ability to go so dang deep within yourself that you are so in tune with what the Spirit of God is doing, paying so much conscious attention to what's important to you and what He's doing within you, that you'll never go without in the world around you because He's already provided everything you need to accomplish what He's given to you!

Let's look at what I call the **"Live to Thrive 5,"** which are the five areas that make up the *whole you*. Each of these five areas is impacted by your dreams, those being: Mind and spirit, health and well-being, career, finances, and relationships and environment. (Go to TheDreamFactoryandCo.com/livetothrive5 to download a FREE one-sheeter of this document.)

I want you to consider where you are currently as it relates to each of these five areas by answering the following questions because it's hard to get to go where you want to be when you don't even know where you are.

Mind and Spirit

Where is your head at most days? What kind of thoughts do you think?

_____

_____

_____

_____

Are your thoughts in alignment with your fears or faith, your doubts or dreams, with where you want to go, or too focused on things of the past? Expound on this.

_____

_____

_____

_____

_____

Where do you put your attention most days? TV, YouTube, social media, God's word? And what are the effects of where you're putting your attention?

_____

_____

_____

_____

_____

Where are you at with the relationship you have with God? Who do you say God is?

_____

_____

_____

_____

What role does He play in your life and in the life of your dreams?

_____

_____

_____

_____

How are you doing with your quiet time?

_____

_____

_____

_____

What's one thing you can do today to support you in having more of a sound mind as you begin your dreaming process?

_____

_____

_____

_____

Health and Well-being

What kind of relationship do you have with food and overall nutrition?

_____

_____

_____

_____

How do you treat your body?

_____

_____

_____

_____

What habits are taking you away from what you want most and what habits are moving you closer toward what you want most?

_____

_____

_____

_____

How do you treat your emotional well-being?

_____

_____

_____

_____

Would you agree that a healthy lifestyle is an important component to living your dreams? Why or why not?

_____

_____

_____

_____

_____

What's one thing you can do today to promote a healthier lifestyle and well-being?

_____

_____

_____

_____

_____

**Dreaming is the least selfish thing you can do;
it's selfish if you don't do it.**

Career

What do you believe about work in general – What does work mean to you, why do you work, what's the value in working, etc.?

_____

_____

_____

_____

Why are you in the career you are?

_____

_____

_____

_____

Is your current career a part of your dreams, or are you doing it just because you've always done it?

_____

_____

_____

_____

What would a dream career actually be?

_____

_____

_____

_____

What's one thing you can do today to move toward the career of your dreams?

_____

_____

_____

_____

Relationships and Environment

Where are you at with the relationship you have with yourself? How do you see you? How do you treat yourself?

_____

_____

_____

_____

Where are you at with the relationship you have with those closest to you—spouse, friends, family, kids?

_____

_____

_____

_____

_____

What do you want most in the relationships around you?

_____

_____

_____

_____

_____

What keeps you from having what you want most out of the relationships around you?

_____

_____

_____

_____

Are the people closest to you dreaming? Why or why not? How does this help or hurt you in your own dreaming process?

_____

_____

_____

_____

Does where you live and the space within your home support your dreams? Why or why not?

_____

_____

_____

_____

Do the things around you influence you more than the dreams within you? Expound on this.

_____

_____

_____

_____

_____

What's one thing you can do today to enhance the relationships around you?

_____

_____

_____

_____

What's one thing you can do today to enhance the environment around you to make it more conducive to manifest the things most important to you?

_____

_____

_____

_____

Finances

What do you believe to be true about money?

_____

_____

_____

_____

Does what you believe about money support you in getting to where you want to be or do you need a new belief system?

_____

_____

_____

_____

Do you see money as helping you or hindering you from getting what you want most?

_____

_____

_____

_____

How much money do you need or want to live out your most real, pure, wildest dreams?

_____

_____

_____

_____

What's one thing you can do today to move toward greater financial freedom?

_____

_____

_____

_____

Now that you've spent some time reflecting on where you are in your journey, are you ready to take that first step towards your dreams? Expound.

_____

_____

_____

_____

Additional Scriptures

TO MEDITATE ON AND CONSIDER:

"I pray that the eyes of your heart may be enlightened in order that you may know the hope to which he has called you" (Ephesians 1:18).

"So if you're serious about living this new resurrection life with Christ, act like it. Pursue the things over which Christ presides. Don't shuffle along, eyes to the ground, absorbed with the things right in front of you. Look up, and be alert to what is going on around Christ—that's where the action is. See things from his perspective" (Colossians 3:1–2, MSG).

"Do you not know that your bodies are temples of the Holy Spirit, who is in you, whom you have received from God? You are not your own; you were bought at a price. Therefore honor God with your bodies" (1 Corinthians 6:19–20).

"Teach me your way, Lord, that I may rely on your faithfulness; give me an undivided heart, that I may fear your name" (Psalm 86:11).

What do these scriptures reveal about the heart of God?

What do these scriptures mean to you?

How could you apply these scriptures to support you in your own journey of dreaming?

Closing Prayer

Dear God,

As I open myself up to You and to this process of dreaming, I ask that You take me even further. I pray that You take me deeper than I could even imagine and that You blow my mind in order to get to my heart. I open myself to You, and I say *YES*. Grant me the courage to change and the wisdom and discernment to know how to change. Show me Your heart. Connect me to Your dreams. In Jesus's name, amen.

CHAPTER 2
The Power of Dreaming
(and Why We MUST Do It)

Pages 29–44

If I were to ask you, "What stops you from living the dream?" What would your answer be? Write your response here:

_____

_____

_____

_____

_____

When most are asked this question, the universal response is, *"Life. Life stops me from living the dream."* If we stop and digest the magnitude of this answer, it's soul-crushing because if *"life,"* or some version of that answer, stops us from living the dream, then what's the point of life?!

"But life happens." Yet, we know, deep down, there has to be more. *There's got to be more, right?!*

Right.

But truth be told, you did stop dreaming, at some point in time, for a myriad of reasons.

For most, our reason for not dreaming starts out innocently enough as a way to "be responsible," to "fit in," to "avoid judgment," to "not face disappointment again," because "there isn't enough time," or "never enough money," and on and on. But then it becomes an *unconscious, learned* state, so it is no longer about not being able to do it; it literally becomes an unlearning of knowing how.

Has this been your experience, and, if so, when did you stop dreaming and why? Consider what or who might have influenced this. What did you see modeled? What were you taught? What did somebody tell you? What was exemplified to you?

_____

_____

_____

_____

Now that you are aware of when and why you stopped dreaming, are you willing to start?

If a willingness to start is step one, positioning yourself to hear is step two. In most cases, it's not that God isn't speaking; it's that we aren't positioning ourselves to hear Him.

My question to you is this: Are you ready to hear? Are you ready to know? Are you ready to get clear? Expound.

_____

_____

_____

_____

_____

_____

_____

_____

_____

_____

"For this people's heart has become calloused; they hardly hear with their ears, and they have closed their eyes. Otherwise they might see with their eyes, hear with their ears, understand with their hearts and turn, and I would heal them" (Matthew 13:15).

The POWER in dreaming!

There are two main reasons dreaming is so powerful.

The first is because your dreams are connected to your heart, not your head.

The Bible says, "Trust in the Lord with all your *heart* and lean not on your own *understanding*" (Proverbs 3:5 [emphasis mine]). There is a reason why. Consider these questions:

Throughout this chapter, what have you learned about the difference between your heart and your head?

_____

_____

_____

_____

Why is your heart such a powerful, profound place to live from?

_____

_____

_____

_____

When your heart speaks, what does it *sound* like? What does it *feel* like?

_____

_____

_____

_____

Explain all the times that you have followed your heart, His leading, intuition, the nudge? What did you notice? How did you know this was from a much deeper place?

_____

_____

_____

_____

Because our hearts hold our dreams, we must have a whole heart so we bring forth whole dreams.

When we consider what whole actually means, we'd conclude that it means **all** of something because we find words like entirety and complete. Whole means that something is in one piece. Therefore, a **whole** heart is a heart in one piece. It's complete, undivided, unbroken, and undamaged, which means it is aligned!

Are you living wholehearted in any area of life? If not, why not? If so, which one(s) and why do you feel whole in those particular areas?

_____

_____

_____

_____

Let's also look at the opposite of a *whole* heart, which sounds more like apathetic, disinterested, indifferent, spiritless, tentative, doubtful, resistant, unwilling, hesitant, reluctant, lukewarm. What about those words? Do any of these words describe how you might be showing up in any area of your life—in your faith, family, career, or community? Be specific.

_____

_____

_____

_____

One of the reasons we don't live with a *whole* heart is because we become blocked. And what blocks us is our hurt. What hurts have kept you blocked?

_____

_____

_____

_____

_____

For many people, hurt is manifested in the form of reasons, excuses, justifications, or even blame. Perhaps it sounds like this: "I want to dream, but …" "I would dream, but …" "I used to dream, but …" What is it for you? *But, what?*

_____

_____

_____

_____

_____

Are you hiding your dreams behind your hurt? If so, why?

_____

_____

_____

_____

_____

Are you hiding your hurt from God? If so, why?

_____

_____

_____

_____

Do you find yourself living in your head more than your heart because of your hurt?

_____

_____

_____

_____

When your head speaks, what does it sound like? What does it feel like?

_____

_____

_____

_____

Are you ready to get out of your head and back into your heart? Why or why not?

_____

_____

_____

_____

Even if your heart feels as though it's been shattered in two or disappointed or mislead, can you still commit to leading with heart? Why or why not? Expound.

_____

_____

_____

_____

The second reason dreaming is so powerful is because you were *created to create*.

Everything starts with a dream. Just because you don't see it or don't have it doesn't mean it's impossible. It just means you haven't created it *yet*.

Do you see yourself as a creator in this life? Why or why not?

_____

_____

_____

_____

What hurdles or current realities feel as though they're in your way to *creating* the life of your dreams? List all the realities that seem to stop you.

_____

_____

_____

_____

How has *not* pursuing your dreams caused negative side effects? Maybe in the form of depression, fear, lack of motivation, needing validation in the wrong places, addiction? Expound.

_____

_____

_____

_____

Do you believe that you can actually *overcome by creating*—meaning, if you don't see "it," create "it?" Expound.

_____

_____

_____

_____

With every dream you create, it's like righting every wrong. By dreaming, you make amends with your past, you trust your future, and you settle into the present moment. You take what you can't see, and you create something you can. What's "impossible" becomes possible, and the pain, in time, is beautifully turned into purpose. It's the most incredible journey you'll take in your lifetime.

What is your greatest takeaway as to WHY dreaming is so powerful?

_____

_____

_____

_____

_____

_____

_____

_____

_____

_____

_____

Additional scriptures

TO MEDITATE ON AND CONSIDER:

"No eye has seen, no ear has heard, and no mind has imagined what God has prepared for those who love him. But it was to us that God revealed these things by his Spirit. For his Spirit searches out everything and shows us God's deep secrets" (1 Corinthians 2:9–10, NLT).

"No, in all these things we are more than conquerors through him who loved us" (Romans 8:37).

"Set your hearts on things above" (Colossians 3:1).

"I consider that our present sufferings are not worth comparing with **the glory that will be revealed in us**. For the creation waits in eager expectation for the children of God to be revealed. For the creation was subjected to frustration, not by its own choice, but by the will of the one who subjected it, in hope that the creation itself will be liberated from its bondage to decay and brought into the freedom and glory of the children of God" (Romans 8:18–21 [emphasis mine]).

"For those who are led by the Spirit of God are the children of God" (Romans 8:14).

"God created mankind in his own image, in the image of God he created them" (Genesis 1:27).

"The thief comes only to steal and kill and destroy; I have come that they may have life, and have it to the full" (John 10:10).

What do these scriptures reveal about the heart of God?

What do these scriptures mean to you?

How could you apply these scriptures to support you in your own journey of dreaming?

Closing Prayer

Dear God,

I see who You have created me to be. I see that You have designed me to have a whole heart. I see that You have created me in Your own image. I now pray that You quiet my head and get after my heart. I say, "Arise! Wake up!" I declare divine alignment. I speak integration. I say, "Yes and Amen," to the things You are doing because I see the true power in everything You do. I see the power of Your hand. I now see the power of dreaming as being the way that I access heaven and bring it to this earth. Grant me a spirit of boldness. In Jesus's name, amen.

CHAPTER 3

The Juxtaposition of Dreaming

Pages 45–52

As you begin the dreaming process, it's important to wrap your head around what I call "the four tools in your toolbox."

Each of these tools is designed to support you in *obtaining* your dreams and guiding you in *sustaining* them. Because let's face it, if having a dream, chasing a dream, and manifesting a dream were easy, we'd all be doing it. And we're not. So let's dive even deeper into your own understanding of what these tools are so you know how to use them on your journey.

We'll begin with our first tool: **Dreaming is a juxtaposition.**

Only we didn't know that.

And it is a major reason why we're not seeing our dreams come true.

A juxtaposition happens when you place two things together that have obvious, ***contradictory*** effects. That means what you're dreaming of and what your current reality says to be true ***are*** going to be two completely different things.

The true value in understanding this tool is the revelation it provides, which is, your current reality— no matter how bleak, how hard, how not ideal it may be—has no bearing on your dreams. However, the *contradictory* effects are likely legit.

You *must* understand that your dreams and your reality are not going to line up on day 1 or even day 365. They're only going to line up when you get through the juxtaposition and cause "what is" to become "what could be." However, these effects can leave anyone feeling discombobulated, no doubt.

What about you? How have the unconscious effects of the juxtaposition stopped you from chasing your dreams?

_____

_____

_____

_____

_____

_____

_____

_____

How has your past stopped you from dreaming about your future?

_____

_____

_____

_____

How is your current reality stopping you from dreaming about your future? I want you to really take inventory and consider: What's going on around you that makes any dream seem illogical, ridiculous, or even unachievable? (Identifying this will help you begin the process of moving through the juxtaposition.)

_____

_____

_____

_____

Your current reality has no bearings on your dreams!

Here are two steps to walk you *through* the juxtaposition:

Step 1: Look at both your dream and your reality *exactly* for what they are, nothing more, nothing less.

Look at your current circumstances exactly for what they are. If you're overweight, you're overweight. If you're broke, you're broke. If you're lacking in motivation, you're lacking motivation. It is what it is. Let it be what it is. State the obvious, without the judgment and criticism of self or others. Let it be what it is.

The good news is, this is just a starting point. And that's all that it is, a starting point. It's hard to get to where you want to be if you don't even know where you currently are.

Go ahead and state the obvious…

_____

_____

_____

_____

_____

Can you accept your reality for what it is and only as a starting point? Expound.

_____

_____

_____

_____

_____

How can the process of looking at things for what they are, without the judgment and criticism of self or others, completely liberate you versus shame you?

_____

_____

_____

_____

_____

Next, write down your dreams. I don't care how big or small those dreams are. I don't care how new or old they may be. I don't care how possible or impossible they may seem. I just want them to be *real* to you. Consider any and every dream you have in all areas of life. Ok, go ahead, write those down:

_____

_____

_____

_____

Can you accept your dreams for what they are? Without judgment? Without comparing them to someone else? Expound.

_____

_____

_____

_____

Your reality will say one thing; your dream will say another. Your head will say one thing; your heart will say another. Fear will say one thing; faith will say something else. God will say one thing; the world will say another. What will YOU say?

Can you look at both your current reality and your dreams, recognize they are both hard, and consciously "pick your hard?" Can you pick the hard that is going to give you what you want most? Expound.

_____

_____

_____

_____

It's likely (and pretty much guaranteed) that the difference between your reality and your dreams is polarizing. It's like oil and water, water and fire. Great. No big deal. It is what it is. Remember, your dreams don't care what your current reality says. But what do _you_ say? Which one, your reality or your dreams, is more deserving of your attention and why? Expound.

_____

_____

_____

_____

Step 2: Pick your hard. When it comes down to two different options or when you're presented with two different choices (i.e., juxtaposition), instead of looking for the easier choice, thinking that your choice should be easy, or that God should just hand you the answer, consciously pick the hard that you want most.

Finally, I want you to write a *realist turned visionary statement* about what you see with your eyes (reality) versus what you see with your heart (dreams, imagination, vision). Take the combined answers from above and write a statement you can read as you begin to move through the juxtaposition. It will sound something like this: "I *realize* that my reality says I have no money, I *realize* that my heart is broken, I *realize* that I have tried and failed a million times, I *realize* that I have a broken marriage … but in my dreams, I *see* abundance because there is more than enough. I *see* a heart within me that is whole and protected. I *see* success because God's already written my story. I *see* …"

It's not what you look at that matters; it's what you *see*. What do you *see*? Write your *realist turned visionary statement* here:

_____

_____

_____

_____

Additional scriptures

TO MEDITATE ON AND CONSIDER:

"Because you have seen me, you have believed; blessed are those who have not seen and yet have believed" (John 20:29).

"Each person should live as a believer in *whatever situation* the Lord assigned to them, just as God called them" (1 Corinthians 7:17 [emphasis mine]).

"And without faith living within us it would be impossible to please God. For we come to God in faith knowing that he is real and that he rewards the faith of those who give all their passion and strength into seeking him" (Hebrews 11:6, The Passion Translation).

"Abram believed the Lord, and he credited it to him as righteousness" (Genesis 15:6).

"Don't worry or surrender to your fear. For you've believed in God, now trust and believe in me also" (John 14:1, TPT).

"I tell you this timeless truth: The person who follows me in faith, believing in me, will do the same mighty miracles that I do—even greater miracles than these because I go to be with my Father! For I will do whatever you ask me to do when you ask me in my name" (John 14:12–13, TPT).

What do these scriptures reveal about the heart of God?

What do these scriptures mean to you?

How could you apply these scriptures to support you in your own journey of dreaming?

Closing Prayer

Dear God,

I am in! As I step out in faith, I ask that You meet me. I ask that You continue to reveal to me the beauty of Your dreams for my life, so it overshadows the pain of my past and the confusion of my current reality. I pray You help me go where I've never gone, help me do what I've never done, and, most importantly, help me to let You lead. I trust You and trust You're using everything to work together for my good, and even when I don't see it with my eyes, I believe it with my *whole* heart. In Jesus's name, amen.

CHAPTER 4

Lifting 'til Failure

Pages 53–60

I'm going to ask you the same question my husband once asked me:

Are you lifting 'til failure?

"Am I what?!" you're probably thinking.

Are you lifting 'til failure in any area of your life? Finding your edge? Getting outside of our comfort zone? Letting go of what you know so you can have what you want? Are you doing that?

This is the second tool in your toolbox of creating awareness: **lifting 'til failure.**

This tool is all about building strength.

We live in a fast-food world, which means it's easy to grow accustomed to having what we want, when we want it. But God and your dreams are not about quick service; they're about character building.

The true value in understanding this tool is being able to recognize that your dreams are going to require strength. Nothing worth having comes easy and not because we have a mean God who wants to make life hard, but because of the character development it offers us.

What about you? Are you "lifting 'til failure" in any area of your life, or are you just lifting until you are sort of, kind of uncomfortable? Be honest and take some inventory on how you're showing up.

_____

_____

_____

_____

_____

_____

_____

_____

_____

_____

As you consider the journey ahead of you, ask yourself: Am I about "quick service" or building my character? Expound.

_____

_____

_____

_____

What habits have you created that are keeping you "skinny" but not supporting you in becoming strong?

_____

_____

_____

_____

"Consider it pure joy, my brothers and sisters, whenever you face trials of many kinds, because you know that the testing of your faith produces perseverance. Let perseverance finish its work so that you may be mature and complete, not lacking anything" (James 1:2–4).

What do you do when you get uncomfortable or when things get hard? What do you do when things aren't going the way that you planned or thought? Expound.

_____

_____

_____

_____

_____

Is your response to the above question getting you to where you want to be? Why or why not?

_____

_____

_____

_____

Consider the areas in your life that you want to change but can't seem to create the change you desire. Is it because you're not "lifting 'til failure?"

_____

_____

_____

_____

What if the challenges and obstacles of life were actually opportunities in disguise? What if the things you call "hard" are actually designed to make you stronger? What if a little pressure was actually good for you?

The Bible tells us very clearly that we are actually to find joy in our trials. Why? Because it's in our trials that we develop perseverance and it's in our perseverance that we build character. We don't build these things when everything is going well. Don't get me wrong, we all love "easy seasons," but anybody can do well when things are easy... But what about when they're not?

Are there any situations in your life right now that are providing you with the opportunity to build strength? If so, what are they, and how can you use these situations to make you and not break you? (NOTE: These situations will feel hard, but they are actually giving you the opportunity to make you better by supporting you in growing your character.)

_____

_____

_____

_____

How can you reframe the hard moments in life to support you in becoming a stronger, better version of you?

_____

_____

_____

_____

What can you do to "enjoy the pressure" even more?

_____

_____

_____

_____

_____

Additional scriptures

TO MEDITATE ON AND CONSIDER:

"I can do all this *through him* who gives me strength" (Philippians 4:13 [emphasis mine]).

"But the Lord stood with me and gave me strength" (2 Timothy 4:17, NLT).

"'My grace is sufficient for you, for my power is made perfect in weakness.' Therefore I will boast all the more gladly about my weaknesses, so that Christ's power may rest on me" (2 Corinthians 12:9).

"'Not by might nor by power, but by my Spirit,' says the Lord Almighty" (Zechariah 4:6).

"May the God of hope fill you with all joy and peace in believing, so that by the power of the Holy Spirit you may abound in hope" (Romans 15:13, ESV).

"Endure hardship as discipline; God is treating you as his children. For what children are not disciplined by their father? If you are not disciplined—then you are not legitimate, not true sons and daughters at all. … No discipline seems pleasant at the time, but painful. Later on, however, it produces a harvest of righteousness and peace for those who have been trained by it" (Hebrews 12:7–8, 11).

What do these scriptures reveal about the heart of God?

What do these scriptures mean to you?

How could you apply these scriptures to support you in your own journey of dreaming?

Closing Prayer

Dear God,

I want to abound in hope! I want my life to be a reflection of You. I don't want to be a "skinny" believer. I want to be strong in You. I don't want the struggle of the journey to overshadow the beauty of the gift You are giving me—a chance to build my character. God, I pray You outshine me. In my moments of weakness, be my strength. When I want to quit, be my sustainability. When I don't know how, be my "how." God, help me to see past current moments, help me to see beyond the obstacles, help me to lean in when I want to lean out, help me to build strength and endurance for Your name's sake. Remind me of *Your* strength. Remind me of my *own*. And teach me to pair it together with You doing Your part and me doing mine. In Jesus's name, amen.

CHAPTER 5

Learning to Acclimate—Getting Comfortable in the Uncomfortable

Pages 61–79

The first two tools in your toolbox of creating awareness—identifying the juxtaposition and lifting 'til failure—are designed to help you *obtain* your dreams. The third tool is designed to help you *sustain* your dreams as you begin manifesting them.

This tool is called **acclimation.**

Most are familiar with this concept as it pertains to climbing, but it is also very relevant to your own growth journey. Just as a climber must adjust to new climates as they climb, so must you.

As you grow, evolve, and gain greater awareness in all areas of life, I want you to realize that an acclimation process needs to happen, which means you'll literally need to let yourself grow accustomed to a new way of doing things.

The true value in understanding this tool is that it is going to give you the ability to adjust to change. Almost every single person would admit they *want* change, but very few actually do. Why? Because change is hard. Change requires you to get outside of your comfort zone. It requires you to go to a different zone, a new condition, a different state of being, a "climate change." And frankly, that is hard.

Think about the last time you underwent a huge amount of change or you even accomplished a goal, but then all of a sudden, you sabotaged your own progress. What happened? How did you respond? Expound.

_____

_____

_____

_____

_____

_____

_____

_____

_____

What about those times you stopped before you even got started because it felt too much, too overwhelming? Expound.

_____

_____

_____

_____

_____

What about those times when you hit some amazing goals and accomplished some amazing feats, but then, for whatever reason, you couldn't seem to sustain your progress? What happened? How did you respond? Expound.

_____

_____

_____

_____

_____

"Therefore, since we are surrounded by such a great cloud of witnesses, let us throw off everything that hinders and the sin that so easily entangles. And let us run with perseverance the race marked out for us, fixing our eyes on Jesus" (Hebrews 12:1–2).

Have you ever quit a habit only to pick it back up again? Why? Expound.

_____

_____

_____

_____

_____

Just like the process of acclimation requires a climber to drop gear at each new camp in order to climb higher, you, too, have to be willing to let go of the things that won't get you to where you want to be. Think about the things in your life that you need to consider not taking with you. These things may have gotten you to where you are, but they won't necessarily take you to where you've never been.

I'd like to suggest that unlike Everest climbers, you aren't acclimating. You're expanding your capacity, but the expansion is too fast for you to keep up with it because even though things on the outside are changing, you aren't changing on the inside and, therefore, can't sustain the "climate change" of life. You must acclimate in each season of your life in order to sustain your continued progress and growth.

What are some things you need to let go of in order to go where you've never gone (habits, unhealthy relationships, negative thoughts, etc.)?

_____

_____

_____

_____

_____

By acknowledging your attachment to all the things that are taking you away from the real manifestation of the dreams inside of you—the distractions, unhealthy habits and behaviors, thought processes and limiting beliefs—you are making your path easier and your burdens lighter, so you can run the race set out before you.

How will you notice your own need to acclimate?

_____

_____

_____

_____

What are you going to do in order to acclimate? How will you take care of yourself?

_____

_____

_____

_____

What got you to where you are won't take you to where you've never been.

A few more things I would like you to consider as you digest all that this chapter offers:

Consider the different "camps" that were referenced in this chapter. Which camp are you currently at and why?

_____

_____

_____

_____

Consider the levels of learning, the "Conscious Competency Ladder." How does your understanding of these levels of consciousness (awareness) and competency (skill level) support you as you set out to try new things?

_____

_____

_____

_____

What did you learn about "liminal space?" What does it mean to you? Give an example in your own life.

_____

_____

_____

_____

How will you recognize when you're in liminal space, and how will you ensure you move through "the space in between" versus just going back to what's familiar?

_____

_____

_____

_____

Additional scriptures

TO MEDITATE ON AND CONSIDER:

"Therefore, since we are surrounded by such a great cloud of witnesses, let us throw off everything that hinders and the sin that so easily entangles. And let us run with perseverance the race marked out for us, fixing our eyes on Jesus, the pioneer and perfecter of faith. For the joy set before him he endured the cross, scorning its shame, and sat down at the right hand of the throne of God. Consider him who endured such opposition from sinners, so that you will not grow weary and lose heart" (Hebrews 12:1–3).

"Do you not know? Have you not heard? The Lord is the everlasting God, the Creator of the ends of the earth. He will not grow tired or weary, and his understanding no one can fathom. He gives strength to the weary and increases the power of the weak. Even youths grow tired and weary, and young men stumble and fall; but those who hope in the Lord will renew their strength. They will soar on wings like eagles; they will run and not grow weary, they will walk and not be faint" (Isaiah 40:28–31).

"Come to me, all you who are weary and burdened, and I will give you rest. Take my yoke upon you and learn from me, for I am gentle and humble in heart, and you will find rest for your souls. For my yoke is easy and my burden is light" (Matthew 11:28–29).

What do these scriptures reveal about the heart of God?

What do these scriptures mean to you?

How could you apply these scriptures to support you in your own journey of dreaming?

Closing Prayer

Dear God,

Teach me how to rely on You. Teach me how to run the race You have set before me while also being in a spirit of surrender to You. Give me the strength to continue when I think I can't, the grace to rest even when I feel like I shouldn't, and the wisdom to know the difference. May I soar on wings like eagles, run and not grow weary, walk and not be faint. I trust You, Lord, and I'm ready to "climb." In Jesus's name, amen.

SECTION 2

CHAPTER 6

Check Your Thoughts—
Your First Step Toward Mastering Your Mind

Pages 81–92

It is now probably obvious to you that it is impossible to live from your heart if you're too busy living from your head. As I said in the book, "Your head is not where your dreams will come from, but it will either *support* you or *hinder* you from the actual process of dreaming."

So how do you get out of your head? How do you actually get out of your own way? Perhaps you've tried mantra's, chanting, even prayer, and maybe it works for a while but given enough time, hours, days, or weeks, you're right back to where you started, and you can hear that self-doubt, worry, and fear creeping up and discouraging you again.

This is our fourth and final tool: **mastering your mind.**

The Bible says, "Do not conform to the pattern of this world but be transformed by the renewing of your mind. Then you will be able to text and approve what God's will is – his good, pleasing, and perfect will" (Romans 12:2). Isn't that what we all want? To know Him? To know His will? To know His good, pleasing, and perfect will? To know the path so we can walk the path?

But that dang head trash!

How do you push past it?

You have to recognize it as trash. As long as you accept it as truth, you will never get rid of it, but as soon as you can see it as trash (gross, disgusting, not-getting-you-anywhere kind of trash), you will get rid of it! But remember this is not a "one and done" kind of deal. If it were that easy, you wouldn't even need this chapter because you'd solve the problem once and be on your merry way. Unfortunately, it doesn't work that way, and just as the trash truck comes every week to pick up your trash, so, too, are you going to have to learn this tool of mastering your mind because you are going to have to use it regularly, daily, even minute by minute. So put this tool with the other three in an easy-to-grab spot, and be prepared to use it!

Now that you've read Chapter 6, what do you see as being the greatest differentiator between your head and your heart?

_____

_____

_____

_____

_____

Which one (your head or your heart) seems to have the driver's seat in your life currently? Expound.

_____

_____

_____

_____

What does the chatter of your head sound like to you? What do you hear? What are your reoccurring thoughts?

_____

_____

_____

_____

_____

"May the words of my mouth and this meditation of my heart be pleasing in your sight" (Psalm 19:14).

When your head does start to chatter at you, how does it make you feel? What emotions come up for you?

_____

_____

_____

_____

How has this chatter gotten in the way or even stopped you from chasing your dreams?

_____

_____

_____

_____

According to cognitive behavioral therapy, your thoughts create your emotions, your emotions create your actions, and your actions create your results.

Thoughts → Emotions → Action → Results

That means your thoughts are ultimately driving your life. Let's take a look.

What are the primary *negative* thoughts that run through your head on any given day?

_____

_____

_____

_____

_____

What emotions do those negative thoughts create within you?

_____

_____

_____

_____

_____

Your thoughts create your emotions, your emotions create your actions, and your actions create your results.

When you feel those emotions, what do your actions (or lack thereof) look like?

_____

_____

_____

_____

What results are your actions giving you?

_____

_____

_____

_____

Do your negative thoughts now explain why you have the results you do? Why or why not?

_____

_____

_____

_____

Let's look at it from a more *positive* perspective.

What are the primary *positive* thoughts that run through your head on any given day?

_____

_____

_____

_____

_____

What emotions do those positive thoughts create within you?

_____

_____

_____

_____

_____

When you feel those emotions, what do your actions look like?

_____

_____

_____

_____

What results are these actions giving you?

_____

_____

_____

_____

**Change your thoughts,
change your world.**

Do your positive thoughts explain why you have the results you do? Why or why not?

_____

_____

_____

_____

_____

_____

_____

_____

_____

_____

Ultimately, this confirms that if we want to change anything, and I do mean anything, you need to start at a thought level.

"We demolish arguments and every pretension that sets itself up against the knowledge of God and we take captive every thought to make it obedient to Christ" (2 Corinthians 10:5).

Note, it doesn't say "take every emotion captive," it says, "take every thought captive."

In Proverbs, it says, "A simple man believes everything, but the prudent man carefully considers his ways" (Proverbs 14:15 World English Bible®). Being "prudent" actually means showing care for the future. It means consciously paying attention to each and every thought, each and every step you take, for the sake of your future. So I wonder, are you showing care for your future with the thoughts you're thinking today? Probably not.

How then do we really take every thought captive? How do we make our thoughts obedient to Christ? This is something I heard all my life growing up but didn't really understand or use until I started to practice what I now preach—**check your thoughts and emotions at the door.** This is the first step in mastering your mind.

Now, when I say, "check your thoughts and emotions at the door," I do literally mean "check," and I want you to consider this analogy: Your thoughts and emotions are information at the door of your understanding, and your home is your life. Your thoughts and emotions will always be gracious enough to knock, but ultimately, you get to decide if you are going to open the door to your home to let them in.

Next, I want you to do a couple of things:

1. On the next page, I want you to draw a house.

2. Then, from your previous answers, around your house, write out your most reoccurring thoughts and emotions, both negative and positive.

3. Next, assess those thoughts. Cross out any thoughts that are not deserving of being in your home and circle the ones that are.

4. To triple-check yourself, make sure the words you circled help you manifest your dreams. Do they support you in becoming the dreamer you were created to be? Are they thoughts that guard your heart so you can live your life free and uninhibited? Are they thoughts that are in alignment with God's word? (NOTE: It's either a "yes" or a "no," there is no in-between.) If so, great! Hang on to those. If not, what thoughts do you need to be thinking so you can achieve your dreams? Add those thoughts around your home.

Your House = Your Life

In order to master your mind, it's going to become your job to check every thought and emotion at the door of your life every single day, heck, every single moment of every single day. Don't ignore them, but also don't just let them in. Hear them, stand with them, process them, and then consciously decide if they're worthy of taking a room within your home. The thoughts that you let into your home will absolutely take a seat in your life. So, though you might be frustrated by your results, you may be discouraged by how you're showing up in your own life, no matter how warranted it all seems, you can absolutely clean up your home (and your life) by starting to use this tool to determine minute by minute, day by day which thoughts and emotions you are going to allow into your life. This will begin the renewal process, and by renewing your mind, you will master your mind.

What would your life look like with a renewed mind?

_____

_____

_____

_____

_____

The hardest day will be the day you begin. The next hardest day is the day you want to quit. Keep at it. Don't quit.

Can you commit to mastering your mind by checking your thoughts and emotions at the door of your life each and every day? Why or why not?

_____

_____

_____

_____

What will it look like for you to actually renew your mind? Give yourself three to five ways in which you proactively intend to do so.

_____

_____

_____

_____

Additional scriptures

TO MEDITATE ON AND CONSIDER:

"Do not be anxious about anything, but in everything, by prayer and petition, with thanksgiving, present your request to God. And the peace of God, which transcends all understanding, will guard your hearts and minds in Christ Jesus. Finally brothers and sisters, whatever is true, whatever is noble, whatever is right, whatever is pure, whatever is lovely, whatever is admirable—if anything is excellent or praiseworthy—think about such things. Whatever you have learned or received or heard from me, or seen in me—put into practice" (Philippians 4: 6–9).

"Do not conform to the pattern of this world, but be transformed by the renewing of your mind. Then you will be able to test and approve what God's will is—his good, pleasing and perfect will" (Romans 12:2).

"May the words of my mouth and this meditation of my heart be pleasing in your sight" (Psalm 19:14).

"Since, then, you have been raised with Christ, set your hearts on things above, where Christ is, seated at the right hand of God. Set your minds on things above, not on earthly things" (Colossians 3:1–2).

"'Teacher, which is the greatest commandment in the Law?' Jesus replied: 'Love the Lord your God with all your heart and with all your soul and with all your *mind*.' This is the first and greatest commandment" (Matthew 22:36–38 [emphasis mine]).

What do these scriptures reveal about the heart of God?

What do these scriptures mean to you?

How could you apply these scriptures to support you in your own journey of dreaming?

Closing Prayer

Dear God,

Forgive me for my wayward thinking. Forgive me for the times that I am unconsciously thinking thoughts that are out of step with You. I didn't even realize how many of my thoughts were out of alignment with You and where I really want to be. As I realign and refocus my attention, I pray that You would speak to me. Show me what's possible. Reveal Your thoughts to me. Wow me with Your majesty in new ways that I may never want to think any thoughts outside of those truths. I pray for Your heavenly renewal on both my head and my heart. In Jesus's name, amen.

CHAPTER 7

Diving into Your Beliefs Part 1—

Belief Formation and the Good Ol' Limiting Belief

Pages 93–117

Well.

That was a lot.

Identifying your limiting belief is one of the deepest steps you can take in creating awareness, and it's also one of your first in building belief. For some, this level of awareness will feel like a lot. Like, a lot, a lot. For others, it will feel like a burden has actually been lifted from you. Neither is right or wrong. It just is.

For me, I unpacked the realness of my limiting belief for a solid four years after I uncovered it. Four years y'all! Then, I spent the next two years simply trying to recognize it when it popped up, so I could stop making decisions with it as my basis of understanding. I have since learned how to deal with it the moment it arises, to clear it *and* move through it—something I will practice until the day I die. As will you.

The good news is everything changes when you understand your limiting belief! It's one thing to know you're stuck. Great. Anyone can do that. Heck, every one of us probably knows that we're stuck, in one area or another. That is not a win. But to really understand why you're stuck is completely freeing.

Once you understand your limiting belief, you're no longer fighting in the dark. It's clear as day.

With all that being said, I have a question I'd really like for you to explore—one question, beyond all other questions, that matters most. And sure, maybe there are some peripheral questions too (I've got plenty of those in the pages to come), but if you answer no other question, this is the one. I beg you, though, do not rush this process. Sit with this. Be still. Let God whisper to you. Connect some dots. Open a few cans of worms. Ask for help. Heck, hire a therapist if need be … I did. I admit, it is a meaty question, and it is one that is very deserving of your time and attention.

Here is my question for you:

What limiting belief do you hold to be true, and how is it stopping you?

_____

_____

_____

_____

There is a lot there.

Here are a few more prompting questions to use as you explore this question even more.

How is this limiting belief getting in the way of your dreams?

_____

_____

_____

_____

_____

How has this limiting belief stopped you when it comes to taking risks?

_____

_____

_____

_____

_____

These waters are deep, no doubt, but if you don't get in the deep waters at some point in your life, you won't ever learn how to swim! And you can't find the truth if you're not willing to wade the waters of lies.

How has this limiting belief stopped you in your career?

_____

_____

_____

_____

How has this limiting belief stopped you in your relationships? With your spouse? Your kids? Your family members? Your friends?

_____

_____

_____

_____

How has this limiting belief impacted your relationship with God?

_____

_____

_____

_____

How has this limiting belief impacted the way that you look at money?

_____

_____

_____

_____

How has this limiting belief impacted your health and well-being?

_____

_____

_____

_____

How has this limiting belief impacted your day-to-day life, just the simple daily activities?

_____

_____

_____

_____

How has this limiting belief impacted your worldview?

_____

_____

_____

_____

How is this limiting belief different than other fleeting thoughts that you have? How can you be more cognizant of the difference?

_____

_____

_____

_____

By now, I hope you can see the impact of your limiting belief. The reality can be hard to look at because you realize how much it's been stopping you in every area of your life.

Until now.

The good news is, it's now the *only* thing keeping you from what you want most, and because you can recognize it, you can change it! This means everyone and everything else is off the hook. You've found the real culprit.

Can you now acknowledge that your limiting belief, which *feels* true, isn't *actually* true? Can you acknowledge that it's just a lie keeping you from what you want most? Expound.

_____

_____

_____

_____

_____

THE VEIL HAS BEEN LIFTED!

As your eyes are opening and your heart is being repositioned, I am going to ask you to do a few things that you may or may not want to do. But it's necessary if you want to be free.

I am going to ask you to repent. Some call repentance a "spiritual matter," and yes, that would be true, but it's so much more than just that. It's a repositioning. It actually turns you from one way of doing things to another, which means it's a chance to rethink and gain a new perspective. It's also the impetus for change because it's a proactive approach to review your own actions and feelings with the commitment to be better. So yes, it is a spiritual matter, but it's also simply a *responsible* and *humane* thing to do. At its core, it's simply your path to freedom.

The *only* thing standing in your way is *not* you; it's the limiting belief you hold to be true.

So grab the tool of lifting 'til failure because I'm going to ask you to do a few push-ups in order to overcome this limiting belief, ok?

Push-up #1: Ask God for forgiveness.
Push-up #2: Forgiveness of yourself.
Push-up #3: Forgiveness towards other people.

With that being said, I could ask if you're ready to repent, if you're ready to forgive, but instead, I will ask you: Are you ready to be free? Are you ready to commit to a personal change? Are you ready to be resolved about living more awakened and aligned? Consider and expound.

_____

_____

_____

_____

_____

If so, then you're ready for repentance. It's time for a few push-ups.

"They don't know, neither do they consider: for he has shut their eyes, that they can't see; and their hearts, that they can't understand" (Isaiah 44:18, WEB®)

Push-up #1: Ask God for forgiveness.

The journey of repentance first starts with understanding the love of God, something most of us really don't understand. Why? Because it blows our minds. It's beyond our cognitive understanding. His love is so deep and so wide and so infinite that our finite perspective doesn't get it. Plus, most have been so busy living from our limiting belief, blaming, shaming, and guilting ourselves for our past mistakes and failures, we can't even receive such a love, so we've just avoided it altogether.

But the reality is, your limiting belief is faulty and it's driving behavior that is outside the will of God for your life and can also be the impetus for many of your ungodly choices. Hence why asking for forgiveness of this thought process is so important.

The Bible says, "If we confess our sins, he is faithful and just and will forgive us our sins and purify us from all unrighteousness" (1 John 1:9). This passage of scripture make it rather clear. If we, you and me, simply confess our sins, acknowledge the wrongdoing, the wayward thinking, then all we have to do is *accept* forgiveness. Too often, we hang onto it. We'll even go as far as asking for forgiveness, but then we walk around in shame because we just won't let it go. It's time to confess our sins *and* to receive His forgiveness.

Can you ask Him to forgive you of your wayward thinking? Can you ask Him to forgive you of your past? Can you ask Him to forgive you of all the things? Expound.

_____

_____

_____

_____

Are you willing? Are you willing to accept His love and cleansing mercies and to turn to a new way of thinking? To a new way of living? Expound.

_____

_____

_____

_____

Psalm 103:12 says, "As far as the east is from the west, so far has He removed our transgressions from us." I'd like you to consider how far the east really is from the west. Can you rest in this assuredness and step into His forgiveness? Expound.

_____

_____

_____

_____

Push-up #2: Forgiveness of yourself.

Once you begin to receive His forgiveness, you will begin to see His love. The next step is to begin to forgive yourself so you can love yourself. Maybe you attest to having a faulty relationship with yourself. Or maybe it's one of flat-out hatred instead of self-love and respect.

In the book of Mark, the chief priests, teachers of the law, and elders ask Jesus, "Of all the commandments, which is the most important?" Jesus responds, "Love the Lord your God with all your heart and with all your soul and with all your mind and with all your strength." He then says, and this is what I want you to really grab onto, "The second is this: Love your neighbor as *yourself.* There is no commandment greater than these" (Mark 12:28–31 [emphasis mine]).

My question to you is this, how much more can we love those around us if we aren't willing or able to love ourselves first?

How are we to be used by God, stepping into our role as the church, when we don't even love ourselves?

In order to love yourself, you have to first forgive yourself. You have to forgive yourself for limited thinking and past behaviors and actions based upon that limited thinking.

"You, Lord, are forgiving and good, abounding in love to all who call to you" (Psalm 86:5).

Can you begin to forgive yourself? If *He* can forgive you, can *you* forgive you? Expound.

_____

_____

_____

_____

_____

How can you proactively forgive yourself today, for your wayward thinking, for your wrong choices, for anything and everything?

_____

_____

_____

_____

_____

"As far as the east is from the west, so far has he removed our transgressions from us" (Psalm 103:12).

I encourage you to spend a few minutes looking at scripture and writing about the truth of His love and forgiveness toward you now. What does God's love say about you? What can you do to lean in even more to better understand the love of the Father so you can know this kind of love for yourself?

_____

_____

_____

_____

Are you willing to accept your own forgiveness? Expound.

_____

_____

_____

_____

Push-up #3: Forgiveness toward other people.

Truth be told, we are so limited in our love for others because we are limited in our love for ourselves. But once you can freely accept His forgiveness while also forgiving yourself, then you are actually liberated to love others, which includes forgiving those who have hurt and wronged you.

The Bible is clear about forgiving others as we, too, have been forgiven. For those of you who face the hard reality that many of your negative experiences were out of your control and involved the very people who should've showed you love and care but ultimately stole your trust and innocence, your next step becomes one of love and forgiveness for others.

Though I will encourage you to forgive with your whole heart, this does not justify what someone did or didn't do. It does not make their behavior right. You see, forgiveness doesn't let someone else off the hook; it lets you off the hook, which is why the Bible talks about forgiveness 121 times. When you learn to forgive, *you* live free. So if you can trust the process and recognize that your ability to forgive has less to do with them and more to do with you, your life will open back up to you.

Who do you need to forgive and why?

_____

_____

_____

_____

How has not forgiving this person impacted you?

_____

_____

_____

_____

Are you willing to forgive so you can be free? Are you willing to *give* the same forgiveness you have *gained*? Expound.

_____

_____

_____

_____

Believe me, I know firsthand how hard this is and because, by now, you have done your fair share of "push-ups," I am going to encourage you to "acclimate." Please refer back to the tool from Chapter 5, so you can simply allow yourself the permission to catch up with this new awareness.

"A new command I give you: Love one another. As I have loved you, so you must love one another" (John 13:34).

Now, before we move on to establishing a better belief, one that actually moves you forward (which we'll do in the next chapter), I want you to do one more thing to really cement this. I want you to write a letter to that younger version of you who lived the negative experience that unintentionally created your limiting belief. In this letter, I want you to do two things:

1. Acknowledge the pain. This means you acknowledge all the pain, all the hurt, and all the disappointment that this "little you" must have (and has) experienced. Bring it all to light. Don't leave anything out. Anything you've avoided saying, have always wanted to say, simply need to say, let it all out. You're writing this letter to release all that pain and to give yourself, maybe for the first time, the care and attention you needed after a difficult experience.

2. Give a new perspective. Once you've acknowledged the pain, I want you to end your letter by giving this "little you" a different way of looking at the experience. We know we can't change what's happened in our past, but perhaps we can change the way we look at it. Maybe had you had a different perspective, you might have navigated the waters of your life differently. Oftentimes, more than a change in circumstances, we need a change in our truth. As you think about the circumstances surrounding your negative experience, here are a few questions I want you to consider:

What words of hope and encouragement did "little you" need to hear in that moment?

What would have provided emotional, spiritual, and mental support to you in the midst of that experience?

If you, right now, could graciously and peacefully come behind "little you" in that moment, whispering a statement of hope and truth, what would you have said to yourself?

What would God's truth have said?

Write your letter here (And please note, you can reference my letter as an example on page 114 in my book):

_____

_____

_____

_____

_____

_____

_____

_____

_____

_____

_____

_____

_____

From the bottom of my heart, I commend you for taking the time to look at the pain most people spend their whole lives running from. By looking at your pain and identifying where it came from and why it's had so much power over your life, you're actually able to heighten your levels of awareness. This level of awareness is both thrilling and challenging. The pro (and con) is now you have no one and nothing else to blame (including yourself). The only thing to point blame at is the limited belief and *that*, thank God, is changeable.

Additional scriptures

TO MEDITATE ON AND CONSIDER:

"God is light; in him there is no darkness at all. If we claim to have fellowship with him and yet walk in the darkness, we lie and do not live out the truth. But if we walk in the light, as he is in the light, we have fellowship with one another, and the blood of Jesus, his Son, purifies us from all sin. If we claim to be without sin, we deceive ourselves and the truth is not in us. If we confess our sins, he is faithful and just and will forgive us our sins and purify us from all unrighteousness" (1 John 1:5–9).

"For our struggle is not against flesh and blood, but against the rulers, against the authorities, against the powers of this dark world and against the spiritual forces of evil in the heavenly realms" (Ephesians 6:12).

"Dear friends, since God so loved us, we also ought to love one another" (1 John 4:11).

"I'll forever wipe the slate clean of their sins" (Hebrews 10:17, MSG).

"Blessed is the one who does not walk in step with the wicked or stand in the way that sinners take or sit in the company of mockers, but whose delight is in the law of the Lord, and who meditates on his law day and night. That person is like a tree planted by streams of water, which yields its fruit in season and whose leaf does not wither—what they do prospers" (Psalm 1:1-3).

What do these scriptures reveal about the heart of God?

What do these scriptures mean to you?

How could you apply these scriptures to support you in your own journey of dreaming?

Closing Prayer

Dear God,

I come to You in a spirit of repentance. I leave my shame, blame, and guilt at Your feet. I leave my limiting belief at Your feet. I confess all my sins and wayward thinking. I acknowledge it, and I let it go. I give it to You, and I ask that You do what only You can do. "Create in me a pure heart, O God, and renew a steadfast spirit within me" (Psalm 51:10). I commit to soaking in Your word. I open myself up to You and Your truth that I might see what I couldn't see before, that I might hear what I couldn't hear before. I acknowledge the ways in which the enemy has tried to blind me and keep me from my place of purpose, blessing, and advancement. I commit to letting go of the lies that I may finally see, know, and experience a new perspective, a divine, heavenly perspective. In Jesus' name, amen.

CHAPTER 8

Diving Into Your Beliefs Part 2—

Understanding and Creating a Limitless Vision

Pages 119–139

If you're like most people, turning the pages from the last chapter to this one, you probably find yourself shouting, "Hallelujah!" Fully understanding a limiting belief can be a lot to digest and a lot to look at, but now having a limitless vision for your life provides so much hope for the future.

Once you can recognize your limiting belief, you can begin the journey of letting it go.

Don't just remove the lie that limits you; grab the truth that frees you.

Statistics have proven that the reason an addict of any kind goes back to their addiction of choice is not that they actually want to, but because:

(a) It's familiar ("a familiar hell").

(b) They don't replace the void with something else ("an unfamiliar heaven").

So the chasm, the space that those choices leave behind, feels extremely large, similar to a gaping hole. Many revert to their old ways because they don't intentionally replace it. They don't fill their time with something fulfilling and progressive. They don't fill the gap.

The same is true for you. Once you identify how much space your limiting belief has taken in all areas of your life, you must concentrate not just on removing it from your life but also on filling yourself back up with something else. But what is that something else?

It's your limitless vision.

Your limitless vision is all about bringing a new world to this current world. It's a world that's "finished" once you get your hands (and heart) on it, a world that you intend to leave behind when you've breathed your very last breath! Your limitless vision is the world you want to live in **and** is the world you are responsible to create.

I know that it *feels* like life has handed you a difficult deck of cards, reality looks bleak, sickness and illness have you down and out, you've been hurt in the past, you just lost your job or you hate your current job, divorce has sideswiped you, disbelief and fear have got you frozen in your daily decision making, and the economy has blown up your plans. Yeah, I get it, but your vision for the future says something different.

So here again, I ask you the meatiest, most loaded question I could ever ask you:

What did you identify as your limitless vision, and how could it change your life forever?

_____

_____

_____

_____

_____

_____

_____

_____

_____

_____

Limitless Vision =

(a) An unbiased, non-attached way to live that allows you to form new ideas and concepts beyond current, external senses and establish a more creative and resourceful approach to life.

(b) Heaven on earth.

Here are a few more prompting questions to use as you explore this question even more.

Are you ready to throw off everything that hinders you so you can run the race toward creating that limitless vision? Are you ready to throw off every limiting belief that entangles you, AND are you ready to point your attention where it needs to be—on your limitless vision? Why or why not?

_____

_____

_____

_____

What would it look like to throw yourself at your limitless vision?

_____

_____

_____

_____

How could your limitless vision support you in your career?

_____

_____

_____

_____

How could your limitless vision support you when it comes to taking risks?

_____

_____

_____

_____

How could your limitless vision enhance your relationships? With your spouse? Your kids? Your family members? Your friends?

_____

_____

_____

_____

How could your limitless vision impact the way that you look at money?

_____

_____

_____

_____

How could your limitless vision impact your relationship with God?

_____

_____

_____

_____

How could your limitless vision impact the way that you treat yourself? Your health? Your well-being?

_____

_____

_____

_____

How could your limitless vision impact the way you look at the world?

_____

_____

_____

_____

How could your limitless vision impact your day-to-day life, just your simple daily activities?

_____

_____

_____

_____

How could your limitless vision support you in manifesting your dreams?

_____

_____

_____

_____

Now that you can see the power of your limitless vision, the next step is making it come alive in your life.

Are you ready to make it *real*?

If so, the first step to making it *real* is making it loud!

That creates the question: What gets your attention?

The answer: Whatever is the loudest!

Whatever is the loudest gets your attention, and whatever gets your attention gets your life.

If your limiting belief is louder than your limitless vision, of course, it is going to get your attention. But if your limitless vision is louder than your limiting belief, then it will begin to get your attention. That means the bigger the vision, the smaller the limiting belief. The goal is to shift your focus and attention to a belief that will actually serve you. The goal is to make your limitless vision so freaking loud that it not only gets your attention but ultimately shapes your life.

I want you to get this limitless vision loud!

- Journal about it
- Meditate on it day and night
- Talk about it with your family
- Put it on your mirror
- Hang it on your fridge
- Put it on your nightstand
- Carry it in your wallet
- Use it as your screensaver!

This may sound crazy, but give it a color and wear that color as often as you can. Give it a smell and let that aroma intoxicate your home. Find a song that reminds you of it and play it all the time. Grab a few Bible verses that embody it and meditate on those day and night.

Get it loud in your life!
Turn the volume up!

How can you make your limitless vision "loud" in your life? Identify five to six ways you can make it real.

_____

_____

_____

_____

_____

_____

"**These commandments that I give you today are to be** _on your hearts_**. Impress them on your children. Talk about them when you sit at home and when you walk along the road, when you lie down and when you get up. Tie them as symbols on your hands and bind them on your foreheads.** _Write them on the doorframes of your houses and on your gates_" **(Deuteronomy 6:6–9 [emphasis mine]).**

Go do that. Like, now. Stop reading and take twenty to thirty minutes, crank up some music, and make your limitless vision come alive. Ready, go!

MUSICAL INTERLUDE …

How good is that?

Now, as your eyes are opening and your heart is being repositioned, you are going to see life in a whole new way. I will encourage you to consciously and constantly pay attention.

You must pay attention!

Why? Because every day, you are going to be given the opportunity, with every circumstance that arises, to proactively choose what you want to believe, either your limiting belief or your limitless vision. Sure, circumstances might be trying to convince you that your limiting belief is true, but what if those same circumstances were also giving you the chance to consciously choose to bring your limitless vision to this earth? Just as you learned to believe your limiting belief, you can also learn to believe your limitless vision, but you must pay attention.

When a hard conversation arises, what will you *choose* to believe, your limiting belief or your limitless vision?

When you lose your job, are you going to *choose* to believe your limiting belief or your limitless vision?

When things don't go as planned, what will you *choose* to believe, your limiting belief or your limitless vision?

When you wake up, before your feet hit the floor, are you going to *choose* to believe your limiting belief or your limitless vision?

When you feel vulnerable, are you going to *choose* to believe your limiting belief or your limitless vision?

The bottom line is every day, in every way, you are given a choice to choose between your limiting belief and your limitless vision, and here's the truth, they both have power. They both will change your life. Which one will you listen to? Which one will have your attention? Which one will you build your life on? Expound on your final thoughts.

_____

_____

_____

_____

_____

Additional scriptures

TO MEDITATE ON AND CONSIDER:

"Where there is no vision, the people perish" (Proverbs 29:18, KJV).

"For the Lord gives wisdom; from his mouth comes knowledge and understanding. He holds success in store for the upright, he is a shield to those whose walk is blameless, for he guards the course of the just and protects the way of his faithful ones. Then you will understand what is right and just and fair—every good path. **For wisdom will enter your heart**, and knowledge will be pleasant to your soul. Discretion will protect you, and understanding will guard you" (Proverbs 2:6–11 [emphasis mine]).

"For in this hope we were saved. But hope that is seen is no hope at all. Who hopes for what they already have? But if we hope for what we do not yet have, we wait for it patiently. In the same way, the Spirit helps us in our weakness" (Romans 8:24–26).

"Finally, brothers and sisters, whatever is true, whatever is noble, whatever is right, whatever is pure, whatever is lovely, whatever is admirable—if anything is excellent or praiseworthy—think about such things" (Philippians 4:8).

"I, the Lord, reveal myself to them in visions, I speak to them in dreams" (Numbers 12:6).

"Sing to the Lord and new song; sing to the Lord, all the earth. Sing to the Lord, praise his name; proclaim his salvation day after day. Declare his glory among the nations, his marvelous deeds among all peoples" (Psalm 96:1–3).

"I was sound asleep, but in my dreams I was wide awake" (Song of Solomon 5:2, MSG).

What do these scriptures reveal about the heart of God?

What do these scriptures mean to you?

How could you apply these scriptures to support you in your own journey of dreaming?

Closing Prayer

Dear God,

Thank You! Thank You for this revelation. Thank You for this vision. I commit to throwing off everything that hinders me, including my limiting belief, and I *wholeheartedly* chase this vision for my life, *Your* vision for my life. As I give You my heavy burdens, I ask for Your yoke, which is easy and light. As I continue to let go of my limiting belief, may I run the race before me with assuredness and boldness. Help me to *be* the change. Help me to bring this vision to earth, not in my own strength but by Your Spirit in me. In Jesus's name, amen.

CHAPTER 9

Finding Your Conviction

Pages 141–162

Now that you've identified a core limiting belief as well as a limitless vision, it's safe to ask the question, "How do I avoid the limit and run toward the vision? How do I build my life around the limitless vision versus around the belief that is blocking me?"

The answer is conviction.

I think most would admit they don't necessarily have a problem *getting* motivated; they have a problem *staying* motivated. Most admit they like the concept of accountability, but few actually *live* accountable. What about you? I'd like you to consider for a second what motivation and accountability looks like in your own life.

"Now faith is assurance of things hoped for, a conviction of things not seen" (Hebrews 11:1, American Standard Version).

Are you having trouble *getting* motivated or *staying* motivated? Expound.

_____

_____

_____

_____

Why do you think your motivation runs out?

_____

_____

_____

_____

What would *lasting* motivation bring to your life?

_____

_____

_____

_____

What about personal accountability? How are you doing in that department?
Expound.

_____

_____

_____

_____

_____

What could personal accountability do for you as you chase your dreams?

_____

_____

_____

_____

_____

Conviction =
(a) The ability to stand *for* something.
(b) Your "I can't not."

I want you to close your eyes, and I want you to consider a few things:

Consider for a second what your life would look like if you had **lasting** motivation and **sustainable** accountability.

Consider having motivation and accountability that doesn't live outside of you or rely on someone or something else.

Consider motivation or accountability that doesn't cost you an arm and a leg.

Consider motivation and accountability that help you live out your vision for the world.

As you reflect, write down what comes to mind. What could be possible?

_____

_____

_____

_____

_____

What if I told you everything you wrote down was possible?!

Well, it is.

You and I both know it is.

It's called conviction.

That means you don't need to be motivated, you don't need an accountability partner, you don't need more opinions, and you don't need to spend more money being inspired by someone else. You need conviction! Conviction is the difference-maker.

Motivation, inspiration, accountability, and drive don't happen from the outside in. They happen from the inside out.

Conviction is being so certain, so unshakable that you don't need evidence or proof. You don't need to be convinced because you already are. Ultimately, this is how you bring an unshakeable, unapologetic, limitless vision to this world. It's through your conviction.

In your own words, what does it mean to have conviction? And how is it different from a preference, opinion, bias, or judgment?

_____

_____

_____

_____

_____

It's time to get rooted.

"Therefore put on the full armor of God, so that when the day of evil comes, you may be able to stand your ground, and after you have done everything, to stand. Stand firm then" (Ephesians 6:13–14).

How is conviction different than a preference, opinion, bias or judgment?

_____

_____

_____

_____

How are your preferences, opinions, biases, and judgments debilitating your strength of conviction?

_____

_____

_____

_____

If your limitless vision is the seed, your conviction is your root system.

Identifying Your Conviction Statement

In this chapter, I talk about how we admire people with honest conviction. We admire people who stand for something bigger than themselves no matter the cost. We admire people who are certain, unshakeable, and completely committed. Who is that for you? Who do you admire most and why?

_____

_____

_____

_____

Being that we know all our results are a byproduct of our belief systems, what do you think this person's greatest belief system was that enabled them to live such an extraordinarily convicted life? They believed something to be true, what was it and how would they encourage you to live?

**NOTE: If you're struggling at all with this part, refer back to the example I give in the book on page 152.

_____

_____

_____

_____

Herein lies your conviction statement.

What did you identify as your conviction statement? Write your answer here:

Live:

_____

_____

_____

_____

How does this conviction statement have the potential to change your life?

_____

_____

_____

_____

How does your conviction have the potential to help you fulfill your limitless vision?

_____

_____

_____

_____

How does your conviction shine brighter than any preference, opinion, bias, or judgment?

_____

_____

_____

_____

Amazing potential.

Once you land on your conviction statement, the tendencies are to feel good, to feel free, clear, and much more aligned. Great. That's what we want. That's what a real conviction statement is designed to do. But if you remember, this is not just about *feeling* good; it's about *being* good. Now that you have your conviction and you see its potential in its purest form, it's time to *do* something with it.

As I always say, it's time to "PROVE IT!"

As you consider your own conviction, I want you to tell me five things you will *start* doing that are in alignment with your conviction. How could your conviction change how you spend your time or who you spend it with? How would this impact the way you make decisions or respond to the people around you? What habits would you pick up? How might this change your career? How could it impact your overall health and well-being? How would this shape your goals? List those five (or more) things here:

1. _____

2. _____

3. _____

4. _____

5. _____

Next, give me five things you will *stop* doing. Do you remember our analogy of climbing Mt. Everest? If you remember, at each base camp, climbers don't add gear; they take it off. Their ascent to the top is about their willingness to let go of the things that no longer serve them. What about you? What are you willing to let go of? What things are you holding onto that are not in alignment with your conviction? What judgments are no longer serving you? What opinions serve your ego but don't serve your progress? What biases have you built that don't give you the freedom and flexibility to live your life from conviction? What habits and routines need to go? List those five (or more) things here:

1. _____

2. _____

3. _____

4. _____

5. _____

Now, I want you to really review everything you wrote down, and I want you to ask yourself a powerful question: *Am I INTERESTED, or am I COMMITTED?*

If you are only *interested* in living from your conviction, you *will* give up, the storms of life will present themselves to you, and you'll look for stage left. It will get uncomfortable, your ego won't like it, and you will find a reason, excuse, or justification to find a way out versus through.

Commitment, on the other hand, means you're in, 100%. It's *complete* loyalty. It's *wholehearted* dedication. The moment you *decide* to be committed (because that's all commitment is, a decision), there's no out, no stage left, no tap-out strategies you could create for yourself, no reason, excuse, or justification that is big enough. Sure, you may have to reroute or reconsider your strategy, but quitting is not an option.

Soooooooo: *Are you INTERESTED or COMMITTED?* How do you know? Expound on your truest answer.

_____

_____

_____

_____

_____

"Therefore, my dear brothers and sisters, stand firm. Let nothing move you. Always give yourselves fully to the work of the Lord, because you know that your labor in the Lord is not in vain" (1 Corinthians 15:58).

Next, I want you to strengthen your conviction and the way you do that is with a little pressure. Your conviction is actually built in all the moments that cause you to "lift 'til failure." If you remember from Chapter 4, this is an important tool in your journey and you're going to need it now.

As you grab this tool, I want you to reflect. I want you to reflect on your life, and I want you to recall the best of the best memories as well as the hardest of the hard, both positive and negative, from as early as you can remember, all the way to today. I call these memories your "conviction-shaping experiences" because I believe they were given to you as a way to strengthen your conviction, if you can see it that way.

What experiences can you recall in your life that maybe, just maybe, were designed to strengthen your conviction?

_____

_____

_____

_____

_____

As you reflect on your conviction-shaping experiences, can you now see how each of them wasn't designed to break you but rather to make you? Do you see how everything has been given to you as a way to strengthen your conviction?

Even now, consider the situations that life is presenting you with that feel insurmountable … Maybe you're up against hard circumstances, maybe you're experiencing a lot of trials, many restless nights. Could these obstacles actually be *opportunities disguised as problems*? Problems that really could strengthen your conviction if you left them? Expound.

_____

_____

_____

_____

_____

Once you recognize life's circumstances are all just opportunities presented to help you strengthen your conviction, I want you to do what most people don't, and I want you to offer up gratitude. Why gratitude? Because now, all of it gives you the chance to become a better, stronger version of yourself and that's worth being thankful for.

So come what may, when obstacles present themselves (because they will), when things don't go as planned (because they won't), when people disappoint you (because they will), when you fail (because you will), how can you offer up gratitude in the midst of it all?

_____

_____

_____

_____

How can you lean in, accept the challenge, do a few "push-ups," and allow the testing of your faith (your conviction) to develop perseverance for what you want most?

_____

_____

_____

_____

_____

True joy comes from knowing that the trials and the testing of your faith **does** serve a purpose. It's not designed to break you, but rather make you. It's designed to develop perseverance within you so you become "mature and complete, not lacking anything." How can that not make you grateful?

How could *you* live in your conviction today, standing *grateful* for all the things that have happened in your life, even in the midst of the hard things?

_____

_____

_____

_____

_____

Here's to you and living convicted!

Additional scriptures

TO MEDITATE ON AND CONSIDER:

"Blessed is the one who perseveres under trial because, having stood the test, that person will receive the crown of life that the Lord has promised to those who love him" (James 1:12).

"Therefore put on the full armor of God, so that when the day of evil comes, you may be able to stand your ground, and after you have done everything, to stand. Stand firm then" (Ephesians 6:13–14).

"With all this going for us, my dear, dear friends, stand your ground. And don't hold back. Throw yourselves into the work of the Master, confident that nothing you do for him is a waste of time or effort" (1 Corinthians 15:58 MSG).

"Be on your guard; stand firm in the faith; be courageous; be strong" (1 Corinthians 16:13).

"Stand firm, and you will win life" (Luke 21:19).

"When the storm has swept by, the wicked are gone, but the righteous stand firm forever" (Proverbs 10:25).

"You will not have to fight this battle. Take up your positions; stand firm and see the deliverance the Lord will give you… Do not be afraid; do not be discouraged" (2 Chronicles 20:17).

"Just as the body is dead without breath, so also faith is dead without good works" (James 2:26, NLT).

What do these scriptures reveal about the heart of God?

What do these scriptures mean to you?

How could you apply these scriptures to support you in your own journey of dreaming?

Closing Prayer

Dear God,

Help me to take my stand. Give me the courage to do something about what I believe in. Help me to no longer back down but to rise up. Help me to no longer be distracted by my or other people's preferences, opinions, biases, or judgments. God, give me Your peace that passes all understanding. Give me Your strength for my own weakness and a boldness to rise up like the lion I am. May the words of my mouth, the meditations of my heart, and the steps taken in faith be pleasing in Your sight. In Jesus's name, amen.

CHAPTER 10

Identifying your Protest

Pages 163–191

You will amplify the strength of your conviction when you recognize that it doesn't stand alone. It has a counterpart, a sidekick, a partner in crime, if you will.

Just as you stand *for* something (conviction), you also stand *against* something.

That something is your protest.

Initially, most struggle with this concept because they don't like the idea of "standing against something." It feels too confrontational, too abrupt, but truth be told, most of us aren't holding the line enough.

Wholehearted Protest =
(a) The ability to stand against something.
(b) The wisdom within the judgment.

Now, when I'm talking about protesting, I'm not just suggesting a big mob of people walking the streets publicly stating their opinion. In fact, I don't think we need more public protests to create change. I think we need more *individualized* change at a much more personalized level, so what I'm suggesting is initiating protests in your own life. And not just any ol' area, but in *every* area where you crave change!

Believe it or not, we are actually called to live our lives standing against the issues that are not in alignment with what God is doing.

Consider for a moment the areas in your life (your faith, family, career, community, and even world) where you desire change. What things don't seem to be working? What issues are being ignored? What strategies are broken? What parts are just unfulfilling? What area in your life needs a change, and it seems as though it just won't change? Write your answers here:

_____

_____

_____

_____

_____

"Put on the full armor of God, so that you can take your *stand against* the devil's schemes" (Ephesians 6:11 [emphasis mine]).

As you can probably agree, those are absolutely issues that need change because they're giving you less than ideal results, so my question to you is this: Why do we allow these sorts of things to continue? Or maybe a better way to ask that question is, why do *you* allow those things in *your* life to continue? Expound.

_____

_____

_____

_____

_____

_____

_____

Do you want to know the honest truth?

It's because you don't hate it enough.

You tolerate it.

As long as you tolerate something, you won't change anything. It's actually your indifference that will kill you.

This chapter is designed to help you develop the ability to create change. That's what a wholehearted protest is all about, taking a stand against the misalignment in order to see change actually happen. A wholehearted protest allows for you to *be* the change, not simply to wish for change.

Starting a healthy, wholehearted protest in any area of your life requires four important ingredients:

1. Processed pain
2. Wholehearted hate
3. Divine love
4. Insane clarity of purpose and passion

Let's look at each of these individually:

1. Processed pain.

Pain left as pain at the doorstep of your life just creates a ripple effect of more pain. Hurt people, hurt people. For a moment, I would like you to consider areas within your life you have not processed your pain. What comes to mind? Expound on what you find.

_____

_____

_____

_____

When you consider your unprocessed pain, are you willing to process it for the sake of your own healing? Why or why not?

_____

_____

_____

_____

_____

Though I am going to give you a few steps to support your healing journey, please know that I am not belittling the process by dumbing it down to a 1-2-3 step guide. There is no guide to this; it's simply giving yourself the space to do so and learning to trust yourself and God in the process. I encourage you to not take this so literally that you become more dependent on the steps, only to miss out on the healing itself.

The first step toward healing is to *hear yourself*.

Sooooooo, what do you need to say about this pain? What do you need to hear about it? Write it all down. Get it all out. You can hang, I promise.

_____

_____

_____

_____

What can you do to hear yourself on a more regular basis?

_____

_____

_____

_____

The second step toward healing is to let the pain actually teach you.

I am a firm believer that if we keep experiencing the same thing over and over again, we aren't learning the lesson. If we aren't learning the lesson, we aren't healing. Your pain will always ping you to try to get your attention. Once you hear it, you can learn from it.

Consider for a moment, what lesson is your pain trying to communicate to you? What is your pain trying to teach you so you can be whole?

_____

_____

_____

_____

How can you begin to *accept* the pain versus *resist* it?

_____

_____

_____

_____

Not only does learning the lesson teach you something, it actually makes you stronger. How can processing your pain and learning the presented lesson(s) make you stronger?

_____

_____

_____

_____

The third step toward healing is to use the lesson to get grounded in truth.

You and I both know that your unprocessed pain has kept you in a lie. Once you can see the lie, you have the ability to then lean into God's truth.

What does God's truth say about the lie you've been believing? Find two or three scriptures that will support you in getting grounded in the truth and expound on the impact that those verses could have in any and all areas of your life.

_____

_____

_____

_____

What can you do proactively to live from these truths each day?

_____

_____

_____

_____

The fourth step toward healing is to give your pain purpose, in word and deed!

Once you know the truth, once you start to feel, see, taste, and touch true revelation, you can't *not* share it.

How can you expand your own healing process by sharing your lessons and insights with others?

_____

_____

_____

_____

What would it look like to lead with an open heart and an open mind?

_____

_____

_____

_____

2. Wholehearted hate.

Wholehearted hate is _processed_ anger. It's _healed_ anger. It enables you to walk down the path of your own healing journey far enough to look back and be able to say, "Yuck! Gross! That was awful. That living hell was trapping me and keeping me from my dreams, purpose, and the life I've wanted to live. I hate that those lies kept me from having what I want. I hate it so much that now, _now_, I am going to do something about it, so neither I nor anyone else has to walk that path again."

For just a minute, I want you to build your "wholehearted hate fire" and notate all the things that you just can't stand for any longer, not even one more day; you *must* see change.

What areas in your life are you just so sick and tired of, to the point of actually hating it enough that you are willing to change it? Not only for your sake but for the sake of those around you?

_____

_____

_____

_____

If you remember, in the last chapter, I asked you a **powerful question:** *Are you INTERESTED, or am I COMMITTED?*

Soooooooo: *Are you INTERESTED or COMMITTED* to take a stand against these things? How do you know? Expound on your truest answer.

_____

_____

_____

_____

3. Divine love.

Divine love realized means living *from* love, not *for* love. When you walk in divine love, you realize how loved you really are. You no longer need anyone or anything else to affirm you in order to feel more loved because you know that you already are, so you live like it. This is divine love. We don't have to earn it, do more to get more, accomplish more, achieve more, or become more to have more of His love. It already is.

What areas in your life have you been doing things *for* love instead of *from* love?

_____

_____

_____

_____

_____

What would it look like to live your life *from* love, not *for* it?

_____

_____

_____

_____

_____

"Though the mountains be shaken and the hills be removed, yet my unfailing love for you will not be shaken nor my covenant of peace be removed" (Isaiah 54:10).

4. Insane clarity of purpose and passion.

Living from a place of insane clarity of purpose and passion means you see a problem, and you *do* something about it. You see pain, and you bring healing. You see division, and you bring unity. Ultimately, you no longer care what someone else is going to do about it. The more important question is, *what are you going to do about it?*

Do you believe that the world is waiting for *you* and *your* solution? Do you believe that God created you to be part of the solution you seek? Expound.

_____

_____

_____

_____

_____

What is one thing you can do even now to bring solutions to the problems you see around you by actually using your processed pain? Who is waiting for your story? Who needs to hear your testimony?

_____

_____

_____

_____

Identifying Your Wholehearted Protest.

In this chapter, I talk about how judgment creates a huge chasm between you and other people as well as you and the change you desire to make. Judgment creates a massive separation and ultimately does more harm than good. How has your judgment of yourself and others actually gotten in the way of you creating change?

_____

_____

_____

_____

Now, let's find the *wisdom within the judgment.*

Who do you identify as the person you judge most and why?

_____

_____

_____

_____

The minute we change the way we look at the people, problems, and the circumstances we face, and we consider our judgments through a place of wisdom and greater understanding, we position ourselves to be change agents.

Being that we know this exercise is not about judging people, nor is it about hating people but rather exposing the mindset around *why* they do what they do, as you reflect, what is the *real* reason this person acts in this way? *Why* do they do what they do? What do they believe about themselves that makes them so "arrogant," "manipulative," "harmful," "not dependable?"

**NOTE: If you're struggling at all with this part, refer back to the example I give in the book on page 180.

_____

_____

_____

_____

This, my friend, is your area of protest. Go ahead and write your protest below.

I passionately protest:

_____

_____

_____

_____

Do you see the potential now? Do you see "the thing under the thing?" Before, it was easy to point fingers in judgment at this person, but now, you're no longer shadowboxing; you can see the root issue. It's not this person you can't stand; it's actually the thought patterns, belief system, and mindset that you can't stand. Expound on the revelation this concept provides.

_____

_____

_____

_____

_____

_____

_____

_____

"Why do you look at the speck of sawdust in your brother's eye and pay no attention to the plank in your own eye? How can you say to your brother, 'Let me take the speck out of your eye,' when all the time there is a plank in your own eye? You hypocrite, first take the plank out of your own eye, and then you will see clearly to remove the speck from your brother's eye" (Matthew 7:3–5).

But before you can create change, we've got to look at why you're pointing a finger in so much judgment. As you learned in my book, there's a reason that your judgment against this person is so harsh. "The thing under the thing" that we can't stand about someone else is the thing we can't stand about ourselves. It's the thing we struggle with ourselves.

Perhaps they have low self-esteem; do you? Maybe they wrestle with mediocrity; do you? They walk in fear; do you? Can you be courageous and willing enough to ask yourself: *Is the thing that this person struggles with also the thing I struggle with?* Expound.

_____

_____

_____

_____

How does this show up in your own life? Expound.

_____

_____

_____

_____

Are you clearly able to see why you hate this so much? It's not just because it's something "they do," it's also something you do. And it's not only the area deserving of the greatest change in their life; it's the area that's deserving of the greatest change in *yours*. I'd like for you to consider what your life would look like if you no longer struggled with "low self-worth" or "fear" or "insecurity" (whatever it is you protest). What would be possible? Expound on your answer.

_____

_____

_____

_____

How can you be more aware when others are in your area of protest, and what can you do to help them instead of judging them?

_____

_____

_____

_____

It's one thing to notice when someone else is struggling with the thing you protest, but what about you? What can you do to be more aware when you're struggling with the thing you protest?

_____

_____

_____

_____

If you remember, your conviction and protest work together. They are partners in crime. How can you proactively use your conviction as a way to overcome the thing in which you protest?

_____

_____

_____

_____

Standing against the area you protest will help you bring about the changes you desire most in your faith, family, career, and community. What are five things you can *start* doing today that are in alignment with your protest?

1. _____

2. _____

3. _____

4. _____

5. _____

What are five things you can *stop* doing today that cause you to fall victim to your protest?

1. _____

2. _____

3. _____

4. _____

5. _____

Once you realize that the area you protest is only a chance to heal and a pathway for a greater purpose, the world opens up to you. You don't feel like you're walking around broken or stuck anymore. You're no longer the victim of someone else's behavior. You don't have to sit in the seat of insanity or judgment, getting the same stuff, different day. You have a way to overcome it by living your conviction and passionately taking a stand against your protest.

It's time to rise up and stand against "the thing under the thing." It's time to drop the opinions that distract you and to focus on the area you are built to solve, to bring change to any area of your life, family, career, community, and even the world!

If you're ready, commit now.

If you're ready, commit here:

I, _____, commit to purposefully and
            (name)

passionately stand against _____.
                                (protest)

I will live honestly in my conviction,_____,
                                  (conviction)

and I commit to no longer complaining, blaming, or gossiping about the

issues that I'm not willing to do something about. I will DO something

about them. I will be a change agent for the greater good to see my vision

come to pass, _____!
                    (limitless vision)

_____
      (signature)

Additional scriptures

TO MEDITATE ON AND CONSIDER:

"He always comes alongside us to comfort us in every suffering so that we can come alongside those who are in any painful trial. We can bring them this same comfort that God has poured out upon us. And just as we experience the abundance of Christ's own sufferings, even more of God's comfort will cascade upon us through our union with Christ" (2 Corinthians 1:4–5, TPT).

"If anyone, then, knows the good they ought to do and doesn't do it, it is sin for them" (James 4:17).

"We have become his poetry, a re-created people that will fulfill the destiny he has given each of us, for we are joined to Jesus, the Anointed One. Even before we were born, God planned in advance *our destiny* and the good works we would do *to fulfill it!*" (Ephesians 2:10, TPT).

"Who will rise up for me against the wicked? Who will take a stand for me against evildoers?" (Psalm 94:16).

"Put on the full armor of God, so that you will be able to stand firm against the schemes of the devil" (Ephesians 6:11).

What do these scriptures reveal about the heart of God?

What do these scriptures mean to you?

How could you apply these scriptures to support you in your own journey of dreaming?

Closing Prayer

Dear God,

Give me the ability to find the wisdom within my judgment and the courage to make the necessary changes. Help me to take my stand against the things that You stand against. Help me to start my own wholehearted protest in any and every area of my life so I might be used by You. Give me the assurance that You've got me, that I am safe and secure to heal fully, to allow Your healing arms to wrap around my very soul, and to unify my mind, heart, and spirit in You, that I may be a change agent for Your name's sake. Use me, Lord. Send me. I'll go. In Jesus's name, amen.

SECTION 3

CHAPTER 11

What are You Dreaming?
Becoming a Conscious Creator

Pages 193–216

At the beginning of the book, I mentioned that dreaming isn't what most people think, which is why we aren't getting as much out of it as we could. Now I think you know what I mean.

In theory, we all like the *idea* of dreaming, but few of us understand the actual responsibility it requires. It requires *all* of you!

But, as promised, the whole goal of this book is to help you identify your dreams so that you can unapologetically chase those dreams, so let's get on with it, shall we?! It's time to dream!

In Chapter 11, I share with you the three steps that really prepare you in taking action toward your greatest dreams—clarifying, verifying, and visualizing. Let's begin with clarifying.

CLARIFY

If we all want clarity on our dreams, why are so few actually clear? Believe it or not, we stay unclear because it's giving us something. Even though we admit we don't like being unclear, it's benefitting us somehow in some way; otherwise, we wouldn't hang onto it. In the book, I talk about three reasons most stay unclear: the need to be right, to not have to take responsibility, to stay comfortable. Which is it for you? Expound on your answer.

_____

_____

_____

_____

_____

Clarity begins with a willingness to be quiet. It's about learning to be still in a very loud world.

The cat's out of the bag! Your reason for staying unclear is giving you something after all, otherwise, you wouldn't hang onto it. How has this reason for staying unclear prohibited you from moving forward?

_____

_____

_____

_____

Would you say that you are honestly ready to get clear now, despite what your lack of clarity has been given you? Why or why not?

_____

_____

_____

_____

Now that you understand a few of the reasons you've stayed unclear and you're honestly ready to be clear, let's look at how you become more clear.

The Bible says, "Be still, and know that I am God" (Psalm 46:10). This is a rather clear formula. Be still, and (then) know.

So, you say you want to know—the answer, your next step, how to clarify your dreams, how to fulfill your dreams, how to overcome a problem or obstacle, and on and on. We all want to know a lot about a lot.

Fair. But I wonder, are we willing to do what it takes?

Are you willing to do what it takes? Are you willing to be still? Yes, no, maybe so?

But if we're being honest, being still is hard because "I've got so much to do, so little time to do it, and I need to keep up with my neighbor and with all the things that everyone else, whom I don't even know, is doing on social media."

Yep. That pretty much summarizes it.

But I think you and I would both agree that it's time to be still.

When was the last time you actually did that? Got quiet? Prayed? Meditated? For real, though. What keeps you from getting quiet? Expound on your answer.

_____

_____

_____

_____

Why do you believe that you're ready to create this space in your life now?

_____

_____

_____

_____

_____

What do you want to get out of this quiet space most? We all have expectations, so what are yours?

_____

_____

_____

_____

There are many benefits to being still, quieting yourself, praying, meditating. What benefits do you see (mentally, emotionally, spiritually, relationally, etc.)?

_____

_____

_____

_____

It's likely that as you begin to create this space, you are going to have to do something different than you've ever done before. Be sure to set yourself up for success by picking a spot and picking a time.

1. Pick a spot! You must learn literally to create the space because it won't create itself. Find a spot—your favorite place in your home, outside in your yard, a beautiful view down the road, anywhere that provides the peace and serenity you need to clear your mind and be still. Where can your spot be?

2. Pick a time! Intentionally block out time on your calendar to make it happen. You can do this early morning before the day's hustle and bustle begins, at the end of your day before you go to sleep, during your lunch break, or even in your car between meetings. What time works best for you? A time that you can stick with each day or week?

The next step is "going in." This is when you hear your heart. As referenced in Chapter 2, this is when you hear your heart. This is where your deep *knowing* resides. It's the still, small voice inside you. It's where your gut and your intuition live. It's that nudge that you feel. It's the very voice of God *in you*, leading and guiding you.

There are three layers to accessing this place:

- The chatter layer

- The constructive layer

- The creation layer

I share a lot of details about each layer in the book so let's take some time to explore the impact they're each having on your own journey of "going in."

Does the explained *chatter* layer freak you out, and you just can't seem to get past all the noise that it brings, so you just don't?

_____

_____

_____

_____

Have you ever ignored the great ideas that come from the *constructive* layer because you were "supposed to keep your eyes closed and not think?" What would be a positive outcome if you actually let yourself capture the essence of this layer?

_____

_____

_____

_____

Has the *chatter* layer stopped you from accessing the *creation* layer? Why or why not?

_____

_____

_____

_____

Many unconsciously or even consciously fear what they'll find in the quiet space. What about you? Do you fear what you'll find in the *creation* layer?

_____

_____

_____

_____

Have you felt like there is a "right" and "wrong" way to be still? To pray, meditate, or journal, so you just don't try?

_____

_____

_____

_____

Being still isn't a one-time thing. It's not a quick fix. It's designed to be something you do for a lifetime.

As you'll notice, once you begin to spend more time in this place, you'll desire it more and more. And as you learn how to quiet your mind, you'll actually be positioning both your head and your heart to be in alignment with one another, which is what creates the space to hear. It's actually in this stillness that you position yourself to hear the answers that were too quiet to hear in a loud world.

The most important part to "going in" and really the greatest expectation you can set for yourself is twofold:

1. **To become a better version of you.** The goal is not to be good at quieting yourself or meditating just to be good at it; it's to be good at you. It's to train yourself in discerning and hearing a real knowing so you can proactively live in greater alignment.

2. **To develop a closeness with God, the Father, the Creator of this universe.** He wants to be in a relationship with you. He wants you to commune with Him.

"It is the glory of God to conceal a matter; to search out a matter is the glory of kings" (Proverbs 25:2). What does that mean? It means that God is not keeping anything from you. It also doesn't mean He's not answering your prayers. It simply means that He wants you to seek Him for more of Him, not for more answers.

"Seek first his kingdom and his righteousness, and all these things will be given to you as well" (Matthew 6:33, NLT).

How can you realign your expectations for your quiet time to become a better version of you and to develop a closeness with God?

_____

_____

_____

_____

_____

Soooooo, what are you waiting for? Will you take the time and create the space? Will you allow yourself to "go in?" To dream? To create your life from the most real, pure, wildest at heart dreams that you have within you? If so, let's do this.

Right here, right now, give yourself the space to practice. Put down this workbook, your pen, and quiet yourself. Don't worry; I will be here upon your return. Be still. Let the chatter layer do its thing, enjoy the constructive layer for what it brings you, and surrender to the creation layer. Dream.

(Quiet place interlude…)

The art of being still is first about learning to create the space. It's about creating an environment around you and within you that enables you to tune into yourself and the Spirit of God that's leading you, while tuning out the rest of the world.

What did you feel? What did you experience? What did you see? What did you notice? (Note: there is no right or wrong. It's just about your experience and documenting that experience so you can learn, grow, and become more aware of the space within you.)

_____

_____

_____

_____

_____

Being still positions you to hear so you can become clear.

The following section is a series of questions (and by series, I mean a whole heck of a lot) designed to support you in your own clarification process. For most, we aren't asking ourselves the right questions, nor are we taking the time to hear our own answers. In the pages to come, I give you more than enough questions to consider with the goal of helping you find your own answers!

My hope is not to bombard or overwhelm you or for you to feel like you have to know every single answer to every single question. My goal is to support you in asking a variety of questions so that you're more likely to find the most real, purest, truest, and wildest at heart answers. With each question, create space and hear your answer. Surrender to the process. Don't judge the answer. Don't rush the process. Simply be still so you can know.

Here's to you creating space to "go in."

Write down your limitless vision.

_____

_____

_____

_____

What would the world look if your limitless vision *was* manifested in the world around you?

_____

_____

_____

_____

What would you be doing more of or less of?

_____

_____

_____

_____

What's possible for you when you're living in your vision? What's possible for other people?

_____

_____

_____

_____

What would be inspiring you? What would be motivating to you?

_____

_____

_____

_____

What dreams would come from this vision?

_____

_____

_____

_____

Write down your conviction statement.

_____

_____

_____

_____

What would your life look like if you were living in your conviction?

_____

_____

_____

_____

How would you show up on a day-to-day basis?

_____

_____

_____

_____

Where would you be spending your time?

_____

_____

_____

_____

What would become more important to you, and what would become less important to you?

_____

_____

_____

_____

What dreams would come from this conviction?

_____

_____

_____

_____

Write down your protest statement.

_____

_____

_____

_____

_____

What would your life look like if you were passionately and unapologetically standing in your protest without fear or judgment?

_____

_____

_____

_____

_____

What would you be doing? What would you not be doing?

_____

_____

_____

_____

What dreams would come from this protest?

_____

_____

_____

_____

_____

What would be happening around you, in your life, family, career, and community?

_____

_____

_____

_____

_____

Consider what heaven on earth really means to you. What would heaven on earth look like?

_____

_____

_____

_____

_____

What would be going on within you?

_____

_____

_____

_____

What would be possible for you? What would be possible for other people?

_____

_____

_____

_____

After considering the answers to all of those questions, I encourage you to continue "going in" by answering another series of questions designed to help you answer the greatest overarching question: WHAT AM I DREAMING?

_____

_____

_____

_____

What's most important to you and why? In your faith, family, career, and community?

_____

_____

_____

_____

_____

If you weren't afraid of being hurt again, what would you do? What would you try? What would you go after? In your faith, family, career, and community?

_____

_____

_____

_____

_____

If you felt loved and supported and didn't need other people's approval, how would you live your life?

_____

_____

_____

_____

If you no longer felt like you had to settle, what would you go after? In your faith, family, career, and community?

_____

_____

_____

_____

What has God put in your heart to do? In your faith, family, career, and community?

_____

_____

_____

_____

Who do you want to *be*?

_____

_____

_____

_____

What do you want to *do* with your time?

_____

_____

_____

_____

What do you want to *have* in this lifetime?

_____

_____

_____

_____

What do you want to *give* (to people and this world as a whole)?

_____

_____

_____

_____

VERIFY

Once you have spent some time clarifying your greatest dreams, the next step is to verify them. I want you to review every single answer you wrote down. Consider how beautifully handcrafted all of those dreams are. If everything you wrote down resonates with you, I want you to do one more thing with these dreams to verify them even more.

I want you to really consider *why* you want these dreams. I want you to honestly and humbly gut check all the reasons why you wrote down what you wrote down. We do this to check your motivation behind each dream and to help you recognize that it's not just about the stuff, the acquisition, the acceptance from other people, or even the accomplishment for the sake of the accomplishment. It's more than that. It's deeper than that.

The real goal behind each and every one of your dreams is to make *you* a better person in the process. It's not about the destination; it's about the process. It's not about the dream; it's about *you.*

It's about you becoming all that God intended for you to be.

I want you to look back at all your answers, and I want you to ask yourself: Why? Why do I want this?

I literally want you to go line by line with each of the answers from any (or all) of the above questions you wrote down and in the blank pages to come, ask yourself (with a complete, written-down answer): *WHY? Why do I want this dream? What is it about this dream that I want most? What is the result really going to give me? How will this dream benefit the people around me? What makes this dream so important to me? Are these dreams in alignment with my limitless vision? Are these dreams in alignment with my greatest conviction? Will they support me in standing against my greatest protest? Are my dreams in alignment with God's Word?* (Your dreams should never contradict the written word of God.)

Do that now and use the space provided to explore all your answers.

_____

_____

_____

_____

_____

_____

_____

_____

We give so much weight to the accomplishment and achievement of our dreams that we begin to convince ourselves that "once I achieve that, have that, earn that, or buy that, then I will be happy. Then I will be fulfilled. Then I will feel complete, validated, loved." This approach will never serve us.

Once you've identified your core reasons for each or all of your dreams and you find the rawness, vulnerability, and true conviction behind *why* you want what you want, it's time to look at those dreams for what they really are.

The dream is not just about the dream. The goal is not just about the goal. It's about *who you become* **in the process.**

I want you to take a couple of the key dreams that you identified, and I want you to ask yourself: *Who* do I have to become so that the dream I so badly desire is just a by-product of who I became?

Example: Let's say you want to be in a passionate marriage. Who do *you* have to become so that your marriage is passionate? Not who does your spouse need to become. Not what does the world have to do to bring this person to you. No, who do you have to become so that this is a natural by-product?

Example: If you dream of writing a book, who do *you* have to become so that publishing a book is a natural by-product? Not that the day all of a sudden gives you more hours or nobody bothers you for six months so you can write (though I admit, I have prayed those prayers), who do you have to become so that book, in your hand, in the hands of countless readers, is just a natural by-product?

Your turn.

Who do you have to become so that your dreams are a natural by-product of the person you're becoming? Write down the depth of your answer(s) here:

_____

_____

_____

_____

_____

_____

_____

_____

VISUALIZE

Visualization is the next step to manifesting your dreams. As you learned, it is also completely underestimated, partially because we've watered it down and partially because we don't actually understand how to use it.

Just as getting clear is a practice of forgetting about the *how* and tapping into the *why*, visualization is a practice that supports you in etching the pictures of your dreams into the very fiber of your being, which enables you to *embody your dreams before they exist.* This allows you to *familiarize* yourself with your dreams before you've even accomplished them. Are you ready to familiarize yourself with your dreams?

Every time you sit down and visualize the life you want and the dreams you have, what you're actually doing is giving yourself the opportunity to feel safe and secure with something you have yet to accomplish.

Try right now. Consider a few of your most real, purest, wildest at heart dreams that you listed from any one of my many prior questions. Close your eyes and visualize them. I want you to *feel* your dreams. I want you to *feel* what it feels like to embody them. I want you to *see* yourself manifesting your dreams. I want you to **see** yourself en route to those dreams. I want you to *feel* the sensations in the body. I want you to envision God and all the angels dancing over you as you chase your dreams. Watch where you light up. Watch as you grow comfortable with what you want. Give it a try, right here, right now.

What do you see? What do you feel? What do you notice? Write it all down.

_____

_____

_____

_____

Visualizing is about learning how to create new mental images of possibilities and dreams.

How can visualization actually support you in accomplishing your dreams?

_____

_____

_____

_____

_____

_____

_____

_____

_____

_____

_____

_____

_____

I encourage you to do this over and over again. The more you visualize your dreams, literally taking the time to embody them, feel them, and see them in your mind's eye, the more familiar they become, and the more familiar something becomes, the easier it is to obtain it because we feel safe in having it!

DREAM REAL

As we close out this chapter and shift into the action-oriented next chapter, here's one last thing I want you to consider as you're reflecting on your dreams, clarifying, verifying, and visualizing them:

Are you **dreaming real?**

Here's why it's so important to dream *real* dreams - when you do, two powerful things happen:

1. Humanity comes together

2. You bridge the gap between yourself and your Creator

1. Humanity comes together.

When you dream real dreams that are bigger than you, it automatically means you will need someone else to help you, and when we work side by side with one another, for a cause and a reason that's bigger than ourselves, we come together as people.

How could the fulfillment of your dreams positively impact those around you?

_____

_____

_____

_____

_____

Have you even considered that people are waiting for your dreams?

_____

_____

_____

_____

Why have you not included other people in your life or dreaming process?

_____

_____

_____

_____

Is there any unprocessed pain that needs to be healed so that you can accept other people's support and involvement? (If so, how can you take the next step in healing?)

_____

_____

_____

_____

_____

The truth is we've all been disappointed, we've all been burned, let down, and have a plethora of reasons as to why "it won't work" and why we "can't depend on anyone," but what if it did work? What if you could trust other people? What are the benefits of letting people in?

_____

_____

_____

_____

Part of the healing process, taught in Chapter 10, is to let the pain teach you something. When we learn the lesson, we actually create strength to move forward. What lessons have you learned in the past (both good and hard) that would support you in moving forward, together, with people?

_____

_____

_____

_____

What are two or three things that you can do today to include more people in your life and in the fulfillment of your dreams?

_____

_____

_____

_____

If all your dreams are within your own strength, then you are solely dependent on yourself. But as you begin to dream _real_ dreams that are bigger than you, it's as if you're opening up a door to heaven.

2. You bridge the gap between yourself and your Creator.

I think the God that's easy to forget about, or that we simply don't know, is the One who wants your dreams to happen more than you do. We have a God who is a dreamer. We have a God who is a Creator. We have a God who wants to work with us to create the impossible. He wants to work *with* you to make your dreams come true.

Do you believe that to be true? Do you believe God wants to work *with* you to make your dreams come true? Why or why not?

_____

_____

_____

_____

_____

Why do you seem to feel the need to do this all on your own accord and strength?

_____

_____

_____

_____

What do you not know about God that you need to learn in order to let Him join you in your dreaming process (or, heck, in life)?

_____

_____

_____

_____

_____

Is there any unprocessed pain that needs to be healed so you can accept His support? If so, how can you take the next step in healing?

_____

_____

_____

_____

_____

How could you invite God into your dreaming process even more and what would be possible if He was included?

_____

_____

_____

_____

What does the Bible say about possibilities when God's involved? What Bible verses or stories confirm your decision to include Him?

_____

_____

_____

_____

Now that you've dreamed real, my friend, it's time to live big!!

Your dreams are not just for your own benefit but also for the benefit of those around you. Remember, a dream "brings about possibilities while considering the needs of those around you." Your dreams will also include those around you.

Additional scriptures

TO MEDITATE ON AND CONSIDER:

"The Lord is my shepherd, I lack nothing. *He makes me* lie down in green pastures, *he leads me* beside quiet waters, he refreshes my soul. *He guides me* along the right paths for his name's sake" (Psalm 23:1–3 [emphasis mine]).

"Every day I will praise you and extol your name for ever and ever. Great is the Lord and most worthy of praise; his greatness no one can fathom. One generation commends your works to another; they tell of your mighty acts. They speak of the glorious splendor of your majesty—and I will meditate on your wonderful works" (Psalm 145:2–5).

"But they who wait for the Lord shall renew their strength; they shall mount up with wings like eagles; they shall run and not be weary; they shall walk and not faint" (Isaiah 40:31, ESV).

"Very early in the morning, while it was still dark, Jesus got up, left the house and went off to a solitary place, where he prayed" (Mark 1:35).

"Search for the Lord and for his strength; continually seek him" (1 Chronicles 16:11, NLT).

"Seek the Kingdom of God above all else, and live righteously, and he will give you everything you need" (Matthew 6:33, NLT).

"There are different kinds of gifts, but the same Spirit distributes them. They are different kinds of service but the same Lord. There are different kinds of working, but in all of them and in everyone it is the same God at work. Now to each one the manifestation of the Spirit is given for the common good" (1 Corinthians 12:4–7).

"It's better to have a partner than go it alone. Share the work, share the wealth. And if one falls down, the other helps, But if there's no one to help, tough! Two in a bed warm each other. Alone, you shiver all night. By yourself you're unprotected. With a friend you can face the worst" (Ecclesiastes 4:9–12, MSG).

"You use steel to sharpen steel, and one friend sharpens another" (Proverbs 27:17, MSG).

What do these scriptures reveal about the heart of God?

What do these scriptures mean to you?

How could you apply these scriptures to support you in your own journey of dreaming?

Closing Prayer

Dear God,

Your word says, "Seek first the kingdom of God and his righteousness, and all these things will be added to you" (Matthew 6:33). I commit to seeking You first. And as I do, I pray that I find You when I seek You with my *whole* heart. May You open my heart, my mind, and my soul to hear You in new ways. May You light up the desires of my heart that are in alignment with You and what heaven is doing, and may You make it ever so real to me. Familiarize Your ways within me. Give me the courage and the boldness to respond to everything You've put within me to do. I commit to never relying on my own strength, but together, with the help of other people and Your mighty hand, I will dream. In Jesus's name, amen.

CHAPTER 12

Dreaming is a Verb—
Turning Dreamers into Doers

Pages 217–232

Now that you've taken the time to get clear on your dreams, clarifying, verifying, and visualizing them, it's time to identify the key component to *manifesting* those dreams.

Here we go, ladies and gentlemen, it's the moment we've all been waiting for: "*How* do we make our dreams come true?"

The simple answer: *action.*

Wholehearted action.

You *do* something.

But let's face it, wholehearted action is hard.

"All hard work (wholehearted action) brings
a profit, but mere talk leads only to poverty"
(Proverbs 14:23 [addition mine]).

What about you? What makes wholehearted action, or any kind of action, hard?

_____

_____

_____

_____

Though clarifying, verifying, and visualizing your dreams are incredibly powerful practices to manifesting your dreams, in and of themselves, they will not change your life. You can clarify, verify, visualize, and even strategize all you want, but without *doing* something about your dreams, there will be no impact on your life. The impetus for change happens when we *do* something with what we've learned. Information is cheap. *Applied* information is a game changer.

The good news is: *Everything* you're wanting is found in taking action. It's literally found in the work you're avoiding. That's where all the magic happens! Soooooo, what are you waiting for?

NOTHING.

That's right.

Absolutely NOTHING.

The only difference between your dreams and reality is called action.

Let's get a bit more granular with this. Tomorrow you wake up, and it's time to move toward your dreams—all the things you wrote down in the last chapter; how do you do that? How do you line out your action steps to ensure they are in alignment with what you want most? How do you ensure you are moving toward your dreams in the midst of competing commitments?

The answer is in your daily check-ins.

Here's what a daily check-in will include (and please refer back to page 227 within the book to get clear on how to do each step):

1. Renew your mind. You need to ensure that your head is in alignment with your heart.

2. Visualize your dreams. This means embodying them to the point of familiarizing yourself with them so you can manifest them!

3. Act like it. This is where we are going to spend the majority of our time.

Act like it.

The point of a daily check-in is to make sure your dreams are louder than everything else on that list. If we're not careful, one day turns into the next, and, slowly but surely, everything else that has been vying for your attention begins to win. Put your dreams on your list first. Otherwise, who else will?

What does it mean to "act like it?"

Your dreams are not just for your own benefit but also for the benefit of those around you. Remember, a dream "brings about possibilities while considering the needs of those around you." Your dreams will also include those around you.

It means you are going to manifest your dreams for tomorrow by acting like it today. You are going to act as though it exists now. Today.

Give it a shot. Pick one of the greatest dreams you have and really think about this dream.

Now, imagine it's done! You've accomplished your dream. Signed, sealed, delivered, it's yours. And the you who has achieved that dream is standing at the finish line talking to the you at the starting line. So this is really a conversation between the *future* you and the *present* you.

The present you asks: How must I think to make this dream a reality? The future you would respond how? Write down your answer.

The future you understands how hard this journey is because at that point, you've put in the time, asked the hard questions, cried the tears, and still found a way to overcome. What would the future you tell the present you about the journey ahead of you? What words of wisdom might the future you give to the present you that makes this journey easier to bear?

_____

_____

_____

_____

What does the future you think about your present fears of making mistakes and failures? What does the future you think about the present you caring about what other people think?

_____

_____

_____

_____

What does the future you think about all the things that the present you claims is standing in the way?

_____

_____

_____

_____

_____

What are a couple key things that the future you did every single day that supported the manifestation of your greatest dream come true? How can the present you start doing those things now?

_____

_____

_____

_____

_____

Though these questions seem a little mind – bending, the goal of them is to get you thinking like tomorrow, today. It's to get you looking at your current circumstances from a different vantage point. We are called to live from eternity, not for it. We are called to live from victory, not for it. We are called to live from love, not for it. These questions are designed to get you living from a complete, whole, eternal perspective. Why? Because this is how you bring heaven to earth, today.

Here are a few other things to consider as you imagine the dreams you are born to bring to this world:

What do you need to learn to get going?

_____

_____

_____

_____

_____

Who do you need to talk to? Who could you call, or who could you reach out to and ask for some help?

_____

_____

_____

_____

_____

If you weren't afraid, what would you do right now?

_____

_____

_____

_____

_____

Who is already doing something like this that you could learn from?

_____

_____

_____

_____

What groups could you join that would support you in your progress?

_____

_____

_____

_____

Would it serve you to hire a coach or mentor to help you see what you can't see? If so, who might that be?

_____

_____

_____

_____

What do you imagine might be the hardest part about accomplishing this dream, and how can you strengthen yourself now to be more prepared?

_____

_____

_____

_____

A dream with no action is no dream at all.

And last but not least, list five to ten things you can do to start moving toward those dreams *today*.

1. _____

2. _____

3. _____

4. _____

5. _____

6. _____

7. _____

8. _____

9. _____

10. _____

When doubt, fear, worry, anxiety, and your limiting beliefs pop up, because they will, don't try to ignore them. Don't fool yourself into believing that you shouldn't be feeling or thinking those things (you are human). Instead, acknowledge what you're feeling, understand why (because you're stepping into an unfamiliar heaven and the mind chatter is only freaking out), and then free it by giving it something else to focus on. Take one action item from the above list and do it.

When you're done with that one thing, do the next thing and then the next.

And then, don't stop.

So there you have it!

You've got a Limitless Vision. You've got a Conviction. You've got a Protest. You've got Dreams. And now you've got a course of action! You, my friend, have got your life back!

The light within you is shining ever so brightly, which is a good thing because the world around you needs the light within you. The world needs who you are created to be. The world needs your dreams. It's time to be bold as lions!

Now, go live.

Alive.

Awake.

Heck, go live like a dreamer—because, guess what? You are.

Additional scriptures

TO MEDITATE ON AND CONSIDER:

"What good is it, my brothers, if someone says he has faith but does not have works? Can that faith save him? If a brother or sister is poorly clothed and lacking in daily food, and one of you says to them, 'Go in peace, be warmed and filled,' without giving them the things needed for the body, what good is that? So also faith by itself, if it does not have works, is dead. But someone will say, 'You have faith and I have works.' Show me your faith apart from your works, and I will show you my faith by my works" (James 2:14–18, ESV).

"But be doers of the word, and not hearers only, deceiving yourselves. For if anyone is a hearer of the word and not a doer, he is like a man who looks intently at his natural face in a mirror. For he looks at himself and goes away and at once forgets what he was like" (James 1:22–24, ESV).

"Let us not love in word or talk but in deed and in truth" (1 John 3:18, ESV).

"'So I say to you: Ask and it will be given to you; seek and you will find; knock and the door will be opened to you'" (Luke 11:9).

"In everything that he undertook in the service of God's temple and in obedience to the law and the commands, he sought his God and worked wholeheartedly. And so he prospered" (2 Chronicles 31:21).

"Do you not know that in a race all the runners run, but only one gets the prize? Run in such a way as to get the prize" (1 Corinthians 9:24).

"And he said to them, 'Go into all the world and proclaim the gospel to the whole creation'" (Mark 16:15, ESV).

What do these scriptures reveal about the heart of God?

What do these scriptures mean to you?

How could you apply these scriptures to support you in your own journey of dreaming?

Closing Prayer

Dear God,

Thank You. Thank You for Your revelation that is alive and active. Thank You for your word that is sharper than any two-edged sword. Thank You for this journey and for Your promise to be with me, no matter where I go. I devote my journey back to You. I give You every dream You've ever given me back into Your care. As I run the race that You have set before me, go before me and behind me, go beside me and within me, go all around me. May I know that You are with me! May You bless me and keep me. May Your face shine upon me and give me peace. May Your favor be upon me and for one thousand generations: my family, children, and children's children. May I be only where You are. May my thoughts be only Your thoughts, my dreams, Your dreams. As I knock, I pray that the door be opened. As I seek, may I find. And as I ask, I pray that I will receive.

God, help me to live bold as lions, and wherever I put my foot, may You give me the land for Your name's sake. May Your light so shine within me that the darkness trembles. May I live, love, lead, and learn with my whole heart as I set my sights on Your heavenly wisdom. God, fan into flame the gift of faith You have given me. May I trust Your lead and rise up like the wings of eagles. May I run and not grow weary, may I walk and not grow faint for You are with me. And as I go, may You reveal great and hidden things. May You blow my mind and get after my heart. And in all of this,

"Our Father in heaven,

hallowed be your name,
your kingdom come,
your will be done,
on earth as it is in heaven.
Give us today our daily bread.
and forgive us our debts,
as we also have forgiven our debtors.
And lead us not into temptation,
but deliver us from the evil one" (Matthew 6:9–13).
In Jesus's name, amen.

ABOUT
JULIA GENTRY

BY THE AGE OF TWENTY-THREE, Julia built a successful company in real estate that bought and sold millions of dollars' worth of investment property only to end up $100,000 in debt. She then rebuilt her career as a business coach, advising hundreds of entrepreneurs on how to build a successful business. She bought the house and nice cars, had a few babies, and obtained "the American dream" only to realize it wasn't her dream. Every night as she crawled into bed, she had this nagging question in the back of her mind: IS THERE SOMETHING MORE?

Then, she had a **"midlife awakening."**

Thankfully, she identified the answer to that question (YES), and she has become a "wake-up call" that the people of the world didn't know they always needed!

As a dreamer, author, business owner, Jesus follower, passionate wife, wild mom of four, and founder of The Dream Factory and Co., she provides a fresh, bold approach to creating greater alignment in life and encourages a more awakened way to live. She is on a mission to create a massive wake-up call that ignites people, outside the walls of the church, to be the light in the dark, the salt of the earth, and to be bold as lions in their faith, family, career, and community.

Currently, we don't know where Julia lives or what she's doing next, but you can be sure it's somewhere between brilliant and insane.

Follow her journey at TheDreamFactoryandCo.com.

Made in the USA
Middletown, DE
13 March 2022